For Dr. Charles Voelker
with admiration
for his valuable
contributions to "our"
field and with
kindest regards,
    James F. Bender
    3/14/41

THE PERSONALITY STRUCTURE
OF STUTTERING

THE
PERSONALITY
STRUCTURE
OF
STUTTERING

BY

J_AMES_ F. B_ENDER_, P_H_.D., C.P.

Chairman, Department of Speech, Queens College
Director of Information,
American Speech Correction Association

C O - A U T H O R :

Speech Correction Manual
Principles and Practices of Speech Correction
Speech in College and Life
Phonetic Readings in American Speech

PITMAN PUBLISHING CORPORATION
NEW YORK *CHICAGO*

Copyright, 1939, by

Pitman Publishing Corporation

ASSOCIATED COMPANIES

SIR ISAAC PITMAN & SONS, LTD.

PITMAN HOUSE, PARKER STREET, KINGSWAY, LONDON, W. C. 2

THE PITMAN PRESS, BATH

PITMAN HOUSE, LITTLE COLLINS STREET, MELBOURNE

27 BECKETT'S BUILDINGS, PRESIDENT STREET, JOHANNESBURG, TRANSVAAL

SIR ISAAC PITMAN & SONS (CANADA), LTD.

(INCORPORATING THE COMMERCIAL TEXT BOOK COMPANY)

PITMAN HOUSE, 381-383 CHURCH STREET, TORONTO

Printed in the United States of America

To Anne

PREFACE

One of the most persistent manifestations of personality is speech. Without it man is not only restricted in social participation, but frequently isolated. Although most people possess the power of speech to a *normal* degree, there is a minority group handicapped in speech. Among the minority group are those identified as stutterers, a contingent that has been widely neglected by educators and physicians, mainly, because the nature of stuttering has been recognized from the earliest times as bordering upon the insoluble. Within recent years, however, renewed efforts have been directed toward understanding the nature of stuttering by endocrinologists, psychologists, psychiatrists, educationists, and others. Often, by necessity, their results have been based upon the study of one isolated facet of personality, upon meager numbers of stutterers, or upon questionable assumptions.

Many of the results of such studies bear upon that field, vigorously and rapidly expanding today, known as the psychology of personality. That many of the results may be interpreted from widely different points of view is at least indicative that the definitions and theories of personality are multiple and varied. Of the various existent "schools" of belief none is more promising than dynamicism. This is true if for no other reason than that it provides a meeting place for such widely divergent "schools" as the endocrinological, psychoanalytical, statistical, anthropological, sociological. The dynamicists look on personality as a dynamic manifestation which finds its roots in original nature and, as the result of countless stimuli, is changed throughout life. They see development as the principal entity common to all *personalities*. This phenomenon begins at conception and persists, through a myriad of changes, until death. To conceive of development as static is to think in terms of paradox. Hence, if we take the point of view that speech—normal and disordered—is coextensive with certain aspects of personality, and if we hold that personality is dynamic, continuously functioning like a revolving kaleidoscope, we cannot successfully generalize about stuttering in relation to personality when our facts are based on a few cases of stuttering of widely disparate ages. What is needed ostensibly is more intensive as well as extensive study based upon large numbers of stutterers at various age levels under as strict control as we can muster. Under such conditions we may then discover some personality entities common to types of stuttering or stutterers—entities that are relatively enduring and unique in organization. Such a procedure, because of the potential help it may unearth, seems worth while. We must not, however, lose sight of the possibility that we may not find common entities. In either event, the knowledge would be enlightening and utilitarian.

In writing this monograph, I have tried to keep three objectives in mind: (1) to present the results of the more recent researches in stuttering, especially those results based upon post-pubertal male stutterers of high educational achievement, namely, college and university students; (2) to report the results of a measurement of certain personality traits among a large group of college, male stutterers; (3) to present a rationale of the etiology of stuttering that in some measure supplies co-ordinating concepts to the current fifteen or more theories of the causation of stuttering.

A word concerning the reasons for selecting college, male stutterers as a group for study seems to be in order. The need for studying large groups of stutterers at the various developmental ages has already been mentioned. College stutterers as a group are approaching physical maturity. On the whole, they are free from the determining influences that vocations may have on personality. They come largely from the same cultural area, having prepared for the liberal arts college. Their common curriculum and the fact that they come, for the most part, from public school systems make for a like background of experiences. They represent a type of intelligence that has succeeded in dealing with abstractions. They have stuttered long enough (since surveys are in agreement that almost all stuttering is first evinced in the first decade of life) to be cognizant of the social significance of handicapped speech. They constitute the most readily available, homogeneous group of stutterers since there are more speech clinics conducted by experts in the colleges and universities than in the secondary or primary schools in the United States. Consequently, results of experimentation with college stutterers are most readily applicable. For these reasons, a large group of college, male stutterers seems to be about as ideal for intensive study as any.

ACKNOWLEDGMENTS

I could not have written this monograph without the help and guidance of Professors Milton Smith, Harry D. Kitson, Rudolph Pintner, and Goodwin Watson. To them is due whatever worth may be found in the study; I alone assume responsibility for whatever shortcomings it may have. I am indebted to a number of other experts for reading the whole or parts of the monograph, especially Professors Magdaleine Kramer, Arthur I. Gates, Gardner Murphy, Percival M. Symonds, Drs. Otto Klineberg, William Blake, and Elizabeth D. McDowell, and Mrs. Jane Dorsey Zimmerman. Their comments and criticisms have been provocative and helpful. To Professor Ralph B. Spence I wish to express my gratitude for his encouragement and many unforgettable kindnesses. Mr. James D. Perry of the Personnel Bureau of the College of the City of New York has been a never-failing source of help, and I am greatly beholden to him, as I am to my former colleagues of the City College Speech Clinic, Mr. V. A. Fields and Dr. Corbin Pennington, for the pleasant and profitable hours spent with them in administering speech examinations. To my many friends and co-workers in the American Speech Correction Association who have helped in countless ways I wish to pay especial tribute. To my wife, Anne Parsons Bender, I am indebted for constant inspiration and for the care and industry she exercised in the preparation of the manuscript.

JAMES F. BENDER
Queens College
March 7, 1939

CONTENTS

xiii

LIST OF TABLES AND GRAPHS

THE PERSONALITY STRUCTURE
OF STUTTERING

Chapter I

The Importance of Stuttering As an Educational Problem

Ubiquity of stuttering in educational systems

There is scarcely an educator in the school systems of this and other countries who is not confronted by the problem of stuttering among students. Whether the educator be an administrator or a classroom instructor, the need of making adjustments or providing help for stuttering students is ever-present. For stutterers are ubiquitous in the school systems as well as elsewhere. According to one authority (181)* the number of stuttering children in the school systems is five times greater than the combined totals of blind people and deaf mutes in the United States. Another authority (73) estimates that there are at least 1,113,000 stutterers in this country. Such figures are based upon restricted surveys, since no nation-wide survey conducted by experts has ever been made in this country. Even though the results vary, as can be seen in Table 1, they indicate unanimously that there are many stuttering children whose condition presents a serious and important challenge to educators.

Stutterers at the college level

That many stutterers do not outgrow their speech handicap is indicated by the results of entrance speech tests conducted in some colleges and universities. Furthermore, there are perhaps no data more reliable on the incidence of stuttering at a given educational level than those included

---

* Numbers in parentheses refer to bibliography on pp. 164-181. (Numbers following colons refer to page references.)

Table 1

ESTIMATES OF STUTTERING CHILDREN IN SCHOOL POPULATIONS

Investigator	Locality	Percentage of Stutterers
Ballard (12)	London, England	1.00
Blanton (29)	Madison, Wis.	0.72
Camp (49)	Grand Rapids, Mich.	2.64
Conradi (55)	Six U. S. cities *	0.87
Francis (77)	Iowa City, Iowa	1.00
Hartwell (238)	Boston, Mass.	0.78
Lindberg (74)	Denmark (rural)	0.9
Louttit, Halls (140)	Indiana	0.77
Parker (164)	Australia (Melbourne)	1.27
Root (182)	South Dakota	1.9
Milisen, Johnson (153)	Iowa	1.3
Rouma (183)	Belgium	1.4
Von Sarbo (74)	Hungary	1.02
Westgard (239)	Denmark	0.61

* Kansas City, Mo.; Milwaukee, Wis.; Cleveland, Ohio; Louisville, Ky.; Albany, N. Y.; Springfield, Mass.

in Table 2, since they represent the results of entrance speech examinations administered by experienced speech examiners. Moreover, these results are indicative that stuttering is an important problem in the realm of higher education.

Table 2

RESULTS OF COLLEGE ENTRANCE SPEECH TESTS *

Institution	Examiner	Period	Percentage of Stutterers among Entering Students
C. C. N. Y.	V. A. Fields	1931-36	1.87 (16)
Dartmouth	C. H. Voelker	1935-36	2.60 (*)
Univ. Minnesota	B. Bryngelson	1931-36	2.70 (*)
Ohio State Univ.	G. Oscar Russell	1937	2.80 (*)
Queens College	J. F. Bender	1937-38	2.00 (15)

* Data supplied by the examiners through correspondence.

The rise of the college entrance speech test and the establishment of college speech clinics is only one piece of evidence showing educators' growing concern about stuttering and other speech handicaps as an educational problem. Perhaps there is no better way to appreciate the ever-increasing importance that educators are placing upon stuttering and allied problems than to review the recent history of the speech correction movement in the United States.

The growing speech correction movement

Prior to the World War most of the speech courses in institutions of higher learning pertained to elocution, oratory, and debating, and were largely offered in departments of English; in the high schools and elementary schools there were no organized speech correction programs. In the second decade of the present century courses in the speech sciences, e.g., phonetics, speech pathology, speech psychology, etc., were gradually introduced into the curricula of such institutions as the College of the City of New York, Cornell, the State Universities of Iowa, Minnesota, Ohio, Wisconsin, and Teachers College, Columbia (16).

In 1928, a number of leading speech correctionists from the fields of education and medicine organized the American Society for the Study of Disorders of Speech, which name was changed to the American Speech Correction Association in 1934 (12). This organization has been largely responsible for crystallizing the interest in speech defects, especially stuttering, through its (1) annual conventions, (2) *Yearbooks*—published annually since 1930 under the editorship of Professor Robert West of the University of Wisconsin—(3) official quarterly, *Journal of Speech Disorders*—founded in 1936 and edited by Professor G. Oscar Russell of Ohio State University, (4) Bureau of Information maintained at Queens College, Flushing, New York.

Stuttering, a subject of dominant interest in scientific journals

To date, one of the prime interests of the American Speech Correction Association has been stuttering. Almost 50 per cent of the articles published in the *Journal of Speech Disorders* and in the *Yearbooks* of the American Speech Correction Association deal with the subject of stuttering. Since the inauguration of the *Journal of Speech Disorders* in March 1936 to July 1938 there were nine issues of that organ. The data presented in Table 3 concern the subjects of articles in the various issues of the *Journal of Speech Disorders* and indicate the importance and interest in stuttering.

Table 3

SUBJECTS OF ARTICLES PUBLISHED IN THE JOURNAL OF SPEECH DISORDERS

Subject	Number of Articles	Number of Issues
Cleft palate	2	2
Foreign accent	2	2
Miscellaneous	3	3
Orthodontia	1	1
Reading disabilities	1	1
Re-education techniques	4	3
Spastic speech	5	5
Stuttering	17	8
Surveys	2	2
Voice disorders	3	2
	40 in	9 issues

Of the various types of speech disorders dealt with in the first nine issues of the *Journal of Speech Disorders*, stuttering was the only subject appearing in each issue, and no subject was written about so often.

A similar conclusion is reached when the *Yearbooks* of

the American Speech Correction Association are studied. These contain the papers presented at the annual conventions. A list of the topics covered is presented in Table 4.

Table 4

SUBJECTS OF ARTICLES IN THE AMERICAN SPEECH CORRECTION YEARBOOKS

Subject	Number of Articles	Number of Issues
Cleft palate	2	2
Miscellaneous	20	6
Hearing	8	5
Reading disabilities	2	2
Re-education techniques	5	2
Stuttering	67	6
Surveys	2	2
Voice disorders	3	2
	109 in	6 issues

The results of a study of the leading publications on speech lead to the inference that stuttering is considered to be the most important problem in the field of speech correction.

The wide-spread interest in stuttering

Another indication of the wide-spread interest in stuttering is shown by the growth of speech correction classes and clinics. Even during the lean years following 1929, when some public systems were forced to drop their speech correction programs, others in larger numbers instituted speech correction, and still others broadened their activities. Cities like New York, Philadelphia, San Francisco, Indianapolis, and Detroit have instituted large speech correction programs and are planning to expand the work.

In 1921, Wisconsin established a state department of speech correction with a director. Thus, communities in

Wisconsin that could not otherwise support aid for stutterers and sufferers from other types of speech handicaps are provided with speech correction facilities. Soon after Wisconsin established a state-wide program of speech correction, California did likewise. In 1937 Missouri also founded a state program of speech correction. At the present time other states, such as Louisiana and New York, are considering the initiation of state-wide speech correction programs.

During the Seventy-fifth Congress, Bill H.R.10175, the so-called Pepper-Boland Bill, was introduced. It was being studied by the appropriate congressional committee when the congress adjourned. Among its provisions was one for granting federal aid on a dollar-for-dollar basis to communities desiring to establish speech rehabilitative programs for stutterers and others afflicted with speech handicaps.

SUMMARY

Thus, there are developments indicative of the widespread awareness among legislators, educators, and research workers of the seriousness and importance of stuttering as a problem that needs urgent solution. It would seem, then, that because of the large numbers of stutterers and because of the nation-wide interest in stuttering as evinced by the recent rapid growth of the speech correction movement, any study that might throw light on the accompaniments of stuttering would be timely and educationally useful.

As a matter of fact, Dr. L. E. Travis, in his president's address at the convention of the American Speech Correction Association in Chicago, January 1, 1936, said: "The primary concern of speech correction is the person ... he who is fully grounded in the speech related sciences well knows that speech is a reflection of the personality of the speaker." In a recent work, President Paul Klapper of

Queens College stressed the importance to educators of recognizing "very fully the extent to which speech faults are identified with personality." (16:vi.) Both authorities, leaders in speech pathology and education, respectively, focus the attention of educators on the relationship of personality to disordered speech. This relationship is likewise stressed in recent speech texts. T. H. Pear's *Voice and Personality* and Elwood Murray's *The Speech Personality* are only two of a number of titles which suggest the present-day interest in the closely related fields of speech and personality.

The research project

Another important consideration is that speech correctionists at the various educational levels are of the opinion that stutterers have more personality problems than do non-stutterers. Some correctionists also believe that stutterers have characteristic personality problems. Hence, all materials that provide for a more complete understanding of the relationships between stuttering and personality factors are eagerly sought. Especially is the need felt at the college and university level where speech correctionists are striving to aid stutterers find optimal adjustment and professional preparation.

Thus, a useful service might be performed by answering the questions: Do stutterers have more disturbances of personality than non-stutterers? Are stutterers afflicted characteristically with certain specific peculiarities of personality?

Answers to these two questions might be obtained by (1) presenting the experimental evidence pertaining to stuttering and personality factors and (2) by conducting further experimentation into the field. Before the evidence is presented, however, it is necessary to consider certain definitions and points of view concerning stuttering and personality.

Chapter II

Survey of Concepts of Stuttering; and Its Relation to Personality

Definitions of stuttering

The word *stutter,* meaning to speak with continued involuntary repetitions of sounds or syllables, first came into usage in the English language about 1570 (189) . The disorder of stuttering, however, is ancient. The Egyptian hieroglyphics include a word for the affliction. Demosthenes was perhaps the most famous of the reputed stutterers living in the Greek civilization, and the Roman Emperor Claudius is supposed to have written about his stutter. Hippocrates and Galen both described stuttering and advocated "cures" for it (111:433).

Today there is marked tendency on the part of some authorities to differentiate between stuttering or stammering as opposed to dysphemia. In such cases, stuttering or stammering refers to the manifestation of an inner psychophysical condition which is dysphemia. Until recently, speech pathologists used the terms "stammering" and "stuttering" to differentiate two kinds of symptoms. The former implied a difficulty in initiating speech sounds; whereas the latter term was used to identify speech marked by a compulsive repetition of sounds. At the present time it is customary to use either of the two terms to identify either kind of symptoms. Although they are now synonyms, American authorities seem to prefer the term "stuttering" and British writers generally use "stammering" (17:247).

As Travis has demonstrated, "Basically stuttering and stammering are the same. Practically, stuttering is characterized by the repetition of sounds, words, or phrases while stammering is characterized by speech blocks. The repetition consists of alternate blocks and releases. It is clonic * activity. In this sense there is no fundamental difference between repeating (clonic) activity and blocking (tonic) activity, the latter being a marked prolongation of the block phase of the former." (228:652.)

While stuttering and stammering are the most common terms met with, many others are used to identify symptoms of arhythmic speech. Kleinfeld lists, in addition to stuttering and stammering, "agitolalia, arhythmic speech, Balbus Blaesus, bégaiement, broken rhythm, choreatic stutter, cryptogenetic stuttering, dysarthria, dysphemia, hysterical stutter, Hottentotism, incipient stuttering, phanerogeneric stutter, primary stuttering, secondary stuttering, spasticity of articulation, speech block, speech hesitation, speech stumbling," etc. (16:241.)

Another term that is frequently encountered in the literature of stuttering is "cluttering." It is often confused with stuttering "because of its rapid, hasty, jerky, arhythmic grouping of phrases and repetition of consonants and vowels, but cluttering does not have the hypertension of the throat muscles." (149:1.) A similar definition of cluttering is used by speech correctionists in the Cleveland, Ohio, Public Schools (53) . A similar concept of cluttering is held by Robbins: "Children who can pronounce correctly by itself every conventional language sound sometimes mispronounce so many words that their speech becomes unintelligible, a speech defect known as agitolalia or cluttering." Stinchfield puts "clutterers" in the category of "types of rapid, overreacting, ineffective speakers." (206:136) .

One other speech disorder must be defined in order to

---

* The reader's attention is called to definitions of technical terms, as used in this monograph, on pp. 157-163.

avoid possible confusion with stuttering: it is "aphonia."
McDowell has summarized the definition of Bluemel (32,
34, 35) and Scripture (187) in these words: "Aphonia is
like stuttering in that it is an inability to produce voice;
it is unlike stuttering in that it is a chronic condition
occurring consistently on all voiced sounds, while stuttering is intermittent, or occurring at spasmodic intervals,
and upon various voiced sounds, sometimes one, sometimes another. Moreover, aphonia is not always accompanied by hypertonicity of the muscles of the throat."
(149:1.)

There are several diseases known to the medical pro-
fession whose symptoms resemble—in part at least—some of
the symptoms of stuttering. Certain motor aphasias are
characterized by hesitation upon words or syllables. The
difference, however, lies in the fact that hesitation is on
both voiced and unvoiced sounds and shows no evidence
of cramps of the muscles which control the organs used in
producing the voice (228:684) (149:2). Other diseases of
the brain, such as Parkinson's Disease, cerebral arterio-
sclerosis, post-encephalitis, and poliomyelitis present symptoms quite comparable to stuttering (228:660), which is
marked outstandingly by "an intermittent inability to produce voiced sounds accompanied by severe cramps of the
diaphragm, larynx, tongue, or all three of these speech
organs." (149:1.)

Symptoms of stuttering classified

If stuttering is viewed broadly as being a disturbance of
rhythm in vocal expressions the symptoms can be classified
under the following:

1. *Gasping breathing.* The breathing is marked by (a)
marked protraction of inspiration, sometimes lasting as
long as ten seconds (42) (228); (b) marked protracted expiration. "During normal speech the expiratory period is

about five times as long as the inspiratory period. During stuttering the former may become fifteen times as long as the latter." (228:656.) (c) Marked inequality in the extent of consecutive respiratory movements. "While it is true that there is variation in the extent of consecutive respiratory movements during normal utterance, the variability assumes pathologic degrees during stuttering." (228:656.) (d) Interruptions of expiratory by short inspiratory movements. "This is a very common finding in the breathing curves of stutterers. A long respiratory interval may become so broken up by inspiratory interruptions that it is scarcely recognizable." (228:656.) (e) Periodic fluctuations of breath pressure. "A periodic fluctuation in breath pressure is evident in many photographic records of the stutterer's speech just before and immediately after tones. These waves occur at a rate varying from 25 to 50 per second both during stuttering and when there are no observable signs of difficulty in speaking. However, they rarely, if ever, occur in the free speech of the normal speaker." (228:657.)

2. *Clonic and tonic spasms.* These spasms appear in the breathing musculature, larynx, and organs of articulation (149:1) (228:652). A tonic spasm of the muscles of respiration may last as long as 20 seconds. In clonic spasms the movements may be as fast as 10 movements per second. (228) (233) (42).

3. *Glottal catches.* There is an extremely brief approximation of the vocal bands before and between tones. An extreme abruptness in the initiation of tones is readily apparent (233) (149).

4. *Tremors.* These may be found not only in the speech mechanism but in parts of the body not directly connected with speech (229) (117).

5. *Tonal rigidity* of the voice with accompanying difficulty to speak words, phrases, or sentences beginning with vowels (149) (42) (229).

6. *Atypical synchronistic movements of the larynx, abdomen, and thorax.* Thus it appears that during stuttering, instead of showing the independent and faster rate of rise and fall which characterizes normal speech, the larynx may move synchronously with the abdomen or the thorax or both (229).

7. *General muscular tension throughout the body, exhibited in clenched hands and toes* (109) (17) (230).

8. *Repetition of sounds, words, and phrases* (149). "Repetition of consonant sounds preceding vowels." (149.) "Inability to speak words, phrases or sentences beginning with vowels." (149:1.)

9. *Speech blocks.* "Special difficulty in emitting short vowels." (149:1.)

10. *Lack of rhythm.* "Disintegration of the movements of the speech mechanism as a whole." (228:659.) The speech movements are sometimes arhythmic. There are such crude, primitive, and fundamental movements as sucking, chewing, masticating, coughing, and vomitive sounds (28).

11. *A general picture of nervousness.* "By and large the stutterer presents a picture of nervousness and tension, especially in speaking situations. The muscles of the face become strained, and the expression is often one of embarrassment. The eyes become stary and the cheek muscles drawn. Quite frequently facial and forehead tics and uncontrollable blinking of the eyelids occur. It may be noticed that most severe stutterers are pale, scared, and tired-looking." (17:247.)

CONCLUSION

In this chapter the literature on stuttering that deals with definition was reviewed. The conclusion seems warranted that the symptoms of stuttering speech have been defined objectively and rather thoroughly.

The need of further definition and research

In order to reply to the questions set forth for study, namely, *Do stutterers have more disturbance of personality than non-stutterers? Are stutterers afflicted characteristically with certain specific peculiarities of personality?*, it is necessary to define and to review the current concepts of personality. This objective is sought in the following chapter.

CHAPTER III

Definitions and Concepts of Personality

Definitions of personality

In present-day usage the word *personality* bears many connotations. Although etymologists are not in agreement as to its derivation—there being at least fifty possibilities (4) —the most frequently mentioned is *persona* which refers to the mask worn by the actor in ancient Greece to identify his role. By logical extension, this meaning has become widely used among laymen as referring to the external appearance and action, e.g., dress, voice, gestures, manners, facial tensions and relaxations, etc. Countless definitions of personality can also be found in the literature of theology, law, sociology, bio-sociology, and philosophy. No field of knowledge, however, is more plenteous in definitions of personality than psychology. Many of these definitions are of the omnibus variety.

Omnibus definitions

A few of the current omnibus definitions from the field of psychology of personality reveal the great variety of viewpoint:

1. "Personality is the sum-total of all the biological innate dispositions, impulses, tendencies, appetites, and instincts of the individual, and the acquired dispositions and tendencies—acquired by experience."—Prince (171: 532).

2. "... the entire organization of a human being at any stage of his development."—Warren and Carmichael (241: 333).

3. "... an integration of patterns (interests) which gives a peculiar individual trend to the behavior of the organism."—MacCurdy (141:263).

4. "... levels or layers of dispositions, usually with a unifying or integrative principle at the 'top.' "—McDougall (150:3).

5. "Personality refers not to any particular sort of activity, such as talking, remembering, thinking or loving, but an individual can reveal his personality in the way he does any of these things."—Woodworth (258:553).

6. "Personality is the dynamic organization within the individual of those psychophysical systems that determine his unique adjustments to his environment."—G. Allport (4:48).

Such definitions, although neat, are not extensive enough to provide for a descriptive framework upon which to unfold a complicated personality manifestation such as stuttering. What is needed ostensibly is a deeper appreciation of the backgrounds from which such omnibus definitions spring. Hence, a résumé of the most widely-held theories of personality structure seems to be in order.

Current theories of personality structure

Of the many current theories of personality structure the following appear most frequently in the literature on the psychology of personality:

The biological point of view. Of the various proponents of the biological interpretation of personality perhaps none has given a more coherent presentation than Jennings (118). His theory is based upon the study of genes. He says: "Temperament, mentality, behavior, personality—these things depend in manifold ways on genes." "It may be safely said that there is no type of characteristics in which individuals may differ that has not been found to depend upon genes." (118:154.) He reasons thus: Since a gene is actually a separable part of the chromosomes, and since genes enter into the production of every bodily cell, every structural characteristic is determined by genes. He assumes, of course, that functioning personality is dependent upon bodily structure. However, he does not state that personality is inherited, but rather that no aspect of personality is free from the influence of heredity. As genes are altered, personality characteristics also are altered. He also admits that environment may influence personality characteristics. Thus, heredity and environment become highly interrelated and together are responsible for the personality. Another important tenet of the biological point of view is that the more directly a personality characteristic is bound to structural inheritance the less modifiable it is.

The behavioristic attitude. Holding an opposite position from the biologists is J. B. Watson, who states: "Give me a dozen healthy infants, well formed, and my own specified world to bring them up in and I'll guarantee to take one at random and train him to become any type of specialist I might select—doctor, lawyer, artist, merchant, chief, and yes, even beggarman and thief, regardless of his talents, peculiarities, tendencies, abilities, vocations, and race of his ancestors." (244:82.) "There is no such thing as an inheritance of capacity, talent, temperament, mental constitution and characteristics." (244:74.)

Here is a theory that, if pushed to the extreme, implies that "normal" structure inheritance does not predetermine functioning personality but that "abnormal" structure may limit the functioning personality. Thus, personality is conceived as being environmentally determined.

*The differential point of view.** Stemming from classical psychology, differential psychology has become perhaps the most active of the contemporary "schools." The differentialists see the psychology of personality as being coexten-

* See *Differential Psychology*, Anne Anastasi. New York, The Macmillan Company, 1937.

sive with the psychology of individual differences. To them the elements of personality are sensations, attitudes, sentiments, abilities, capacities, etc.—processes in general that have been accepted by general psychology. In short the differentialists describe personality in terms of standard categories. Their chief interest in personality study is in one facet of the complex at a time. After the facet or attribute has been selected for study, the range and distribution of this attribute within the population of subjects employed are determined. Sometimes a further step is added: the degree of covariation between two or more attributes or functions thus determined is obtained. Hence, statistics may be said to be the main tool of the differentialists, and their concepts of personality are often described in terms of mean, median, mode, standard deviations, coefficients of correlation, multiple correlation, partial correlation, factor analysis, etc.

*Psychoanalytic point of view.** The psychoanalysts conceive of all personalities as being subserved by the same structure: first of all there is the hierarchy of Id, Ego, Super-Ego, which, in terms of general psychology may be translated roughly into emotional impulse, self-consciousness, and conscience, respectively; second, there are the uniform mechanisms such as repression, fixation, regression, etc.; then, there are common emotional experiences, such as Oedipus Complex (male), Elektra Complex (female), guilt, anxiety, latent and manifest dream experiences, bungling acts, sublimations, and the like.

Unlike the differentialists, the psychoanalysts hold a qualitative view of personality. They seek to understand a pattern of behavior. Their approach to the study of personality—psychoanalysis, which deals with the examination of single persons during prolonged sessions by means of

* See *Psychopathology of Everyday Life,* S. Freud. New York, The Macmillan Company, 1914.

"associated thinking"—precludes the use of standardized tests of the differential type.

The typological point of view. The typologists attempt to account for the variety in human nature. They deal with abstracted attributes which are found in only certain people. One of the most widely read typologists is Kretschmer (133). It will be recalled that he maintains that there are four main types of body structure, namely, pyknic, leptosome, athletic, and dysplastic. The pyknic type is marked by: shortness of limbs; compact, rotund, well-nourished torso; delicate bones; soft musculature with fatty tissues abundant; head, chest, and abdomen are large in circumference; narrow shoulders; short neck, soft broad round face; flat skull vertex; facial features well-formed; short, broad, soft hands; soft, thin hair and early baldness; profuse hair of face and body; smooth and ruddy skin. When these characteristics are less pronounced in a body build, the individual is called a pyknoid.

The leptosome type is characterized by generalized deficiency in volume or thickness without corresponding decrease in height; long, narrow, flat thorax; narrow shoulders; long limbs and neck; thin and delicate bones, muscles, skin; small head which tends to be either high or round; long nose; small, receding chin; marked angularity of profile; short egg-formed face; pale skin. When these characteristics are highly pronounced the individual possessing them is identified as an asthenic or sthenic type.

The athletic type is recognizable by strong skeletal development and prominent musculature: broad shoulders, narrow hips; slender lower limbs; coarse bones; prominent cheek bones; strong chin; steep, egg-shaped face.

The dysplastic type falls well outside the typical form; dysplastics, according to Kretschmer, "even impress the laity as rare, surprising, and ugly." (133:65.) The dysplastic type is frequently identified by eunuchoidism and amazonianism; pronounced length of extremities or dwarfism;

broad hips in men; narrow hips in women; unusual distribution of fat, etc.

Kretschmer recognizes admixtures of the various types, such as leptosome-athletic. Further, he links body-type with psychological-type. He states:

"(1) There is a clear biological affinity between the psychic disposition of the manic depressives and the pyknic body type.

"(2) There is a clear biological affinity between the psychic disposition of the schizophrenes and the bodily disposition characteristic of the asthenics, athletics, and certain dysplastics.

"(3) And vice versa, there is only a weak affinity between schizophrene and pyknic on the one hand, and between circulars (manic-depressives) and asthenics, athletics and dysplastics on the other." (133:36.)

Not all typologists deal with body-types. For example, Jung (122) has a theory of psychological types—introvert, extrovert, ambivert. He believes that people are born with the predisposition toward introversion or extroversion. The introvert is one whose interests are directed inwardly, who is likely to be moody, reticent, and greatly introspective, given to autistic thinking. He is largely egocentric, i.e., concerned with his own thoughts and desires and given to day-dreaming and absent-mindedness. The opposite type, the extrovert, is identified by action, gregariousness, loquacity, and a dominating interest in things of the external world. In between the two extremes of introversion and extroversion is ambiversion. The ambivert, who comprises the largest group, is neither strongly introverted or extroverted; his personality traits are marked by an admixture of introversion and extroversion. Jung further believes that ambiversion results from education of the original predisposition toward either introversion or extroversion. Since Jung's original statement of psychological types there have appeared many other definitions of introversion-extroversion. For example, a recent definition provides for five divisions: social introversion, emotional introversion, masculinity-femininity tendency, rhathymia, thinking introversion.

The typologies of Kretschmer and Jung represent only two typological concepts; there are many others.

The gestalt point of view. Within recent years there has developed a school of belief that emphasizes the need of studying the manifestations of personality as a whole or pattern (gestalt) rather than as constituencies or segments. Its main concern is the study of functional networks as they affect the life of the individual. To the gestaltist's way of thinking a score in relation to norms does not reveal very significant understanding of the individual's personality. Köhler (130) has pointed out, for example, that while it may be enlightening to study one hundred hearts as a group, a single heart, as a functioning unit, has more in common with a pair of lungs than it has with other hearts. In other words, understanding of the individuality must be based upon the study of the functions of a personality manifestation as they affect and are affected by other functions of the *same* individuality and not as they may be related, through abstraction, to the manifestations of different individualities. Another tenet of this philosophy is that the personality is not only well-structured, but that it is perceived as well-structured. Köhler's remarks on this point are revealing: "I think it was Nietzsche who occasionally said that sometimes the 'you' is earlier than the 'I.' This seems to apply most of all to our knowledge of 'character' and 'personality,' since it is extremely difficult to get a definite picture of our own character from our subjective experiences, whereas the main traits of the character of others may sometimes be strikingly apparent in their attitude. I do not think that the language of others is our main or most trustworthy cue, in the sense that the content of it might be taken as a description of their experience. (i.e., inferences from verbal cues are not a primary guide to understanding.) People do not talk sincerely about their subjective experiences, and we ascribe to them pomposity or modesty, friendliness or coldness, without their telling us a single word about such traits. In a foreign country, we appreciate to a great extent that others are 'provocative' or 'kind' though we may be absolutely unable to understand their language. Where we do understand the words, their *manner* of talking is often a better cue, and we trust it more than the content of their talk. Also a certain kind of silence can occasionally tell us more about others than any number of words could reveal in the same situation." (130:234.)

The purposive point of view. William James once said: "The Me, like every other aggregate, changes as it grows." This statement puts into a nutshell the view of the purposivists, sometimes called dynamicists, concerning personality. From the individuality of motive springs the personality, say the purposivists. As stated by one of the leaders of this belief, Woodworth, this individuality of motive springs from common instincts. The manifestations of these common instincts change in the maturation process from largely inchoate, inconsistent expressions of personality in childhood into distinct and well-defined motivational systems in adulthood. Thus, the mature personality becomes characterized by sophisticated and stable interests, centralized convictions and habits of expression, precise actions, well-defined goals, and sure evaluations.

The personalistic point of view. Growing out of the purposive or dynamic attitude of personality, there has recently developed a new point of view, personalistic psychology. A recent presentation of this point of view is given by Gordon Allport: "The logical culmination of interest in the individual is the creation of a personalistic psychology. The chief tenet of this school of thought is that every mental function is embedded in a personal life.

In no concrete sense is there such a thing as intelligence, space perception, color discrimination or choice reaction; there are only *people* who are capable of performing such activities and of having such experiences. It is improper to speak of the growth of skill, or vocabulary, or of knowledge; there is no growth excepting in the *person;* it is part of *his* development that skill is enhanced, that vocabulary and knowledge are extended. Nor can motives ever be studied apart from their personal setting, they represent always the striving of the total organism toward its objective." (4:18.)

The conflict of theories

While there are some common elements in some of the points of view of personality structure presented here, they represent widely divergent and often irreconcilable beliefs. There may well be much truth in all of them. Their proponents have been compared to the blind men who described an elephant from their tactual impressions of it: one man felt the elephant's side, and declared the animal was like a wall; a second felt a tusk, and said that the elephant was like a spear; a third touched the trunk, and thought that the animal was of the reptile species; a fourth grasped an ear, and said that the animal was fan-like; a fifth examined the elephant's leg, and compared the elephant to a tree; the sixth felt the tail and declared the elephant was like a rope. All of them were correct so far as they went.

Broadly speaking, it is more reasonable to endorse those theories of personality structure that stress the whole rather than those that conceive of the personality as an agglutination of more or less independent facets. In other words, personality is more than the sum of its individual traits. Hence, we may conclude that such points of view as the gestalt or the personalistic are on the whole more tenable than those of such schools as the behavioristic and the psychoanalytic.

However, to date, psychologists have not been greatly successful in reporting studies of the whole personality. Adequate ways and means for studying pervasive personality patterns have not been devised or made applicable. Nonetheless, there is wide-spread optimism in the ultimate outcome, for psychologists have been working and are working on the assumption that the organized whole of personality is not unanalyzable. In describing it psychologists have frequently listed its various manifestations in anatomy, physiology, intelligence, personality traits, etc. The most common classification of aspects of personality is: morphology, mental capacity or ability, and temperament. Of the three divisions the one about which there is least agreement, especially in reference to definition and measurement, is temperament.

A definition of temperament

Just as there are multitudinous definitions of personality so are there many definitions of temperament. However, since the differences are not so great in the latter as in the former, we may adopt one definition as a convenience: "Temperament, like intelligence and physique, might be said to designate a certain class of raw material from which personality is fashioned. Strictly speaking there is no temperament apart from personality, nor any personality devoid of temperament. It is merely convenient to employ the term in speaking of dispositions that are almost unchanged from infancy throughout life (dispositions saturated with a constant emotional quality, with a peculiar pattern of mood, alertness, intensity, or tonus). The more anchored a disposition is in native constitutional soil the more likely it is to be spoken of as temperament. It is seldom doubted today, any more than it was among the ancients, that temperament is dependent somehow upon the biochemical constitution. Work dealing primarily with glands, physical build, or blood composition frequently claims to be seeking the biological foundations of *personality*. And so it is—indirectly; but first of all it is seeking the physical correlates of temperament." (4:53.) Thus, temperament "refers to the characteristic phenomena of an individual's emotional nature, including his susceptibility to emotional stimulation, his customary strength and speed of response, the quality of his prevailing mood, and all peculiarities of fluctuation and intensity in mood; these phenomena being regarded as dependent upon constitutional make-up, and thereby largely hereditary in origin." (4:54.) The various aspects of temperament are commonly referred to as traits of temperament or personality traits. These personality traits are many and varied, at least in name, for Allport and Odbert have reported over 11,000 trait names from Webster's New International Dictionary (7).

There are at least three points of view regarding traits of temperament and their measurement among psychologists today.

The trait hypothesis point of view

The trait hypothesis, which underlies the personality tests and inventories of Allport (5), Heidbreder (107), House (113), Pressey (170), Strong (211), Bernreuter (20), and others pretends to deal with genuine components of personality. A main assumption is that generalized and complex dispositions offer a plausible picture of personality. Personality traits are conceived as personal dispositions overlapping one another in structure and in function but nevertheless identified by focal characteristics and basic drives or purposes. Psychologists who hold the trait hypothesis point of view are usually dynamicists, purposivists, or personalists. To the anti-traitists, they would say, it may well be true that personality is composed of many specific habits, but running through them are certain basic "motifs." For example, they might admit that a person may be neat about his clothing but untidy about his desk. But these are opposite manifestations of a more basic trait —egotism, which can be measured as such. Hence, special groups of traits may be studied, such as generalized interests, attitudes, values, etc. According to two outstanding representatives of the trait hypothesis point of view, "Although traits are strictly personal and unique forms of adjustment, a few seem common enough to be regarded as comparable from one individual to another. These are scalable traits, such as Ascendance-Submission, Introversion-Extroversion, Perseverance, etc." (7:15.) If a community of traits does exist, how much more common and characteristic should they become as the result of a common handicap, such as stuttering!

Adherents to the trait hypothesis have of course used personality tests of the pencil and paper variety. Of the recent tests of that type, none has been more widely used than the Bernreuter Personality Inventory.

The anti-trait point of view

Still other psychologists hold that personality is an agglutination of countless specific habits. Hence, no true generalization concerning personality traits may be made about the individual. For instance, it is untenable to those who hold this point of view to measure a general trait such as neatness, for a man may be neat about his person but slovenly about his room. Or, a child may be honest in making change, but dishonest in writing an examination paper. Thus, any attempt to measure a generalized personality trait by a personality inventory may be fraught with failure from the outset because personality is conceived as being composed of millions of specific habits.

It should be borne in mind that the anti-trait point of view is based to a great extent upon the studies of children, such as Hartshorne and May's *Studies in Deceit,* in which it is shown that the dishonesties of children are highly specific. In a later work, *Studies in the Organization of Character,* they maintain that with maturation the integration of behavior can be accomplished gradually in proportion as systems of response are attached to principles, laws, ideals, as well as to concrete demands of immediately perceived situations. In other words, the anti-trait point of view is especially applicable in dealing with the young personality, according to the leading proponents of this belief.

It is also interesting to note that some of the leaders of this "school" of belief use personality inventories in making trait studies. Symonds and Jackson (215), for example, have constructed and used an inventory for students in the secondary school. The items of their inventory are composed of questions which refer to specific situations. Because of their specificity and because they are addressed to older children, the items are said to be more valid than if they referred to generalities or were addressed to younger children. Many of the current personality tests, such as the Bernreuter Inventory, are composed largely of items that refer to specific situations.

The point of view of pure or unique traits

The point of view of the "pure traitists" may be summarized in the words of Lorge: "To be useful in psychology a trait must be regarded as freed from the influence of other traits." (137:273.) A more extensive statement of the "unique traits" point of view is given by Flanagan, who states: "The ideal theory of personality would:

1. Define its elements without ambiguity and in terms of behavior.
2. Be founded on extensive and accurate observations.
3. Consist of basic elements which are independent.

4. Provide a simple explanation of the maximum number of well-established facts.

5. Have the maximum predictive value." (72:3.)

This point of view is held widely by those who use empirical and statistical methods in evaluating instruments for measuring personality traits of the inventory type. Independence of traits, i.e., purity or uniqueness of traits, is obtained by statistically determining the overlap between scales and then by rescoring the scales according to the number of non-correlating factors that they have been found to contain. Usually two and not more than three factors are derived. For example, Flanagan studied the Bernreuter Personality Inventory by factor analysis. He found, by using the statistical methods of Hotelling (112), that "The scores on the four scales, viz., Neurotic Tendency, Self-Sufficiency, Introversion-Extroversion, Dominance-Submission, of the Bernreuter Personality Inventory may be largely accounted for in terms of two factors. The first factor is similar to the trait measured by the tests of Neurotic Tendency and Introversion-Extroversion and has been termed 'Self-Confidence.' The second factor has most in common with Bernreuter's Self-Sufficiency and, reversing the sign, has been designated 'Sociability,' indicating the opposite of non-sociability or independence." (72:77.)

Those psychologists who believe that factor analysis falls short of describing personality frequently mention that, by its very nature, personality is so complicated that it is impossible to think of any "factors" that are really unrelated to others. However, there are a few personality tests, such as the Bernreuter Inventory, that may be scored from the points of view of the "traitists" as well as the "pure traitists." Thus, the results obtained from using them may be interpreted from either or both points of view.

"Pen and pencil" tests are not, of course, the only methods of studying personality. If the common descriptive classifications of personality are retained, i.e., morphology (covering physique and physiology), mental capacity and ability, temperament, the various methods of personality study may be put into three respective categories.

1. *Methods of studying morphology.* In this category can be placed all the methods commonly used by anatomists, endocrinologists, physiologists, when studying human beings. Taking a cephalic index of a person, analyzing his blood chemistry, recording vasomotor conditions are only three of many techniques used in studying the human personality as reflected by morphology.

2. *Methods of studying mental capacity and ability.* Although there is no uniformity of opinion regarding the definition or nature of intelligence, intelligence tests are widely used. The so-called I.Q. (intelligence quotient) test is administered to individuals, usually below 14 years of age. It may be verbal or of the performance variety. Also there are group intelligence tests, most of which are of the verbal kind. In addition to intelligence tests, there are literally thousands of others that pretend to measure specific mental abilities. A large proportion of this type may be classified as achievement tests. In a wide sense, too, tests of musical talent, perseveration, and other capacities may be called mental tests.

3. *Methods of studying temperament.* The personality inventory has already been alluded to as being a frequently used instrument for measuring personality traits or traits of temperament. The study of various types of records, case histories, etc., offers a way of measuring personality. Rating scales or judgment blanks are also used. These then comprise a large group which may be lumped together as standardized tests. To this group might also be added the association tests of Jung, Kent and Rosanoff, and others. Finally such techniques as hypnosis, automatic writing, psychoanalysis, and others might be called methods of studying temperament since they are directed toward a clearer understanding of the emotional life of the person.

Taken as groups, it may be concluded that the first, i.e., methods of studying morphology, are the most reliable, principally because such methods deal with essentially stable aspects of personality. The second group, while not so reliable as the first group, are yet more reliable, on the whole, than the third group. As Terman has pointed out, "Indeed personality" tests are "in about the stage that intelligence testing was passing through in the nineties of the last century. We are not measuring personality, but exploring with improvised tests . . . to see how people respond." (217:606.)

These various methods of personality study are frequently used by psychologists of the various "schools." Many of the methods, especially those of the first two groups, have been used in studying stutterers.

A working hypothesis

By definition and symptomatology stuttering is a disorder of oral communication which plays a dominant part in personality manifestation. We posit that stuttering entails personality maladjustments; that these personality maladjustments may be characteristic. With these assumptions and with the outlines of the current psychologies of personality in mind, we turn to the experimental literature on stuttering to find corroboration or refutation in the three main divisions of personality, namely, morphology, mental capacity, and temperament. We are especially interested in trying out the hypothesis on stutterers of like age and sex since these two factors, especially the former, are frequently mentioned by authorities as being largely determining of the quantity, as well as the quality of personality adjustments or maladjustments. In other words, we shall hold as constants, stuttering, age, and sex; we shall study the reports of experiments that deal with post-pubertal, male stutterers.

CHAPTER IV

Personality Structure of Stutterers: Morphology

Upon the assumption that the *organized whole* of personality is analyzable, research workers and experimentalists in the field of speech pathology and allied fields have produced evidence that, when amassed, leads to the conclusion that stutterers tend to differ from non-stutterers in many aspects of personality. Those studies and researches that deal with morphology of stutterers (including physique, physiology, motor co-ordinations, and the like) are significantly revealing.

Stutterers tend to have characteristic physique

Travis, Malamud, and Thayer (232) studied 43 male stutterers ranging in age from 15 to 38 years, and 128 male non-stutterers from 17 to 37 years of age. The data were obtained by (1) general observations of body form, (2) anthropometric measurements, (3) evaluations of personality characteristics. Kretschmer's (133) body-type categories were used, and the evaluation of personality characteristics was based on Jung's (122) classification of psychological types of introvert and extrovert.*

With Kretschmer's and Jung's definitions in mind, Travis, Malamud, and Thayer report the results of their study as given in table on page 32.

Of the leptosomic group of stutterers, 17, or 74 per cent, were found to be introvertive and 3, or 13 per cent, to be extrovertive.

* See pages 19-21.

Body Type	No. of Cases		Percentage of Entire Group	
	Stutterers	Normals	Stutterers	Normals
Leptosome	23	11	48.6	8.7
Leptosome-Athletic	13	20	27.9	15.5
Athletic	4	48	8.6	37.5
Pyknic	0	8	0.0	6.2
Pyknoid	4	9	8.6	7.1
Dysplastic	3	32	6.3	25.0
	47	128	100.0	100.0

Four results of this study are especially pertinent: (1) stutterers were found to be mainly leptosomic body build; (2) not one stutterer among the entire group was diagnosed as pyknic; (3) very few stutterers were found to be dysplastic; (4) there was a high percentage of introverts among the stuttering group. It is also interesting to note the high percentage of dysplastics appearing in the control group.

Until sounder evidence to the contrary is advanced, the conclusion of this study that male stutterers tend to be unique morphologically must be accepted.

Stutterers have characteristic biochemistry

The biochemical studies of stutterers have differentiated them from non-stutterers in a variety of ways.

Stratton studied urinary creatine and creatinine as indices of the metabolism of a sub-breathing stammerer. He found that: "Times of excitement are accompanied by less creatinine and more stammering . . . the more nearly the creatinine coefficient approaches the normal and maintains it, the better the speech performance. It is believed that in sub-breathing stammerers, if the urinary creatinine coefficient is low, it may be concluded that an important factor in the etiology of stammering is a faulty metabolism and this must be corrected to effect a cure." (210:325.)

Trumper experimented with 101 cases of stuttering at the University of Pennsylvania Speech Clinic and discovered a correlation between the stutterers' breathing patterns and the red cell count and the hemoglobin content. His finding of a high erythrocyte count in the stutterers' blood is especially important in the light of W. B. Cannon's researches that erythrocytes are increased during emotional changes and that the increase is due to a sympathetic stimulation of the spleen. Thus, the high blood sugar content is believed to be indicative of the emotionality of the stutterer. Trumper also states that the scarcity of female stutterers is due largely to the lower viscosity of their blood which in turn results from a lower red cell volume (235).

Although, as Glaser's survey (93) has shown, there is lack of uniformity of opinion among practicing endocrinologists concerning the relationship of stuttering to the functioning of the ductless glands, two pieces of research are illuminating. Browning (41) traced the etiology of stuttering to the involution of the thymus gland, and Gordon (94) has reported that stuttering resulted in four patients to whom excessive amounts of thyroxin were administered.

Starr selected saliva as a research medium reflecting metabolism of the body rather than blood or urine. Especially was he interested in the hydrogen ion content of saliva as a metabolic index. (A hydrogen ion is an atom of hydrogen bearing a single positive electric charge.) Using 228 "healthy, normal subjects" as controls, he found that the 610 specimens of saliva contributed by the controls ranged from pH 5.95 to pH 7.25 with 86 per cent of the specimens within the limits of pH 6.55 to pH 7.00 inclusive. The mean was pH 6.78; the median, pH 6.80. "When the salivary pH was 6.60 or less, the individual appeared fatigued or deficient in the amount of energy at his disposal; when the salivary pH was about 7.00 the individual appeared to have an abundance of energy at his disposal." (196:399.) Subsequent experiments with the controls proved: (1) "that the hydrogen concentration of the mixed saliva increased when the individual was fatigued"; (2) "the findings pointed practically invariably to a steady decrease in salivary pH during the afternoon"; (3) "when a subject was emotionally excited his salivary pH increased regardless of the time of day." (196:401.)

After Starr had experimented upon the controls, he analyzed 200 samples of saliva obtained from 58 sub-breathing stutterers—diagnosed as such by speech clinicians. The mean, mode, and median for the salivary pH of the 58 sub-breathing stutterers were 6.00, 6.10, 5.90 and 6.00, whereas for normal individuals they are 6.8, 6.8 to 6.9, and 6.8, respectively. Starr also found that the stutterers were "overloaded with CO_2 (carbon dioxide) in their saliva, far in excess of the normal individual." (196: 406.)

Pursuing his line of research further, he obtained a group of "ten distinctly psychopathic stutterers" from the speech clinic, tested their saliva, and found the pH content to be between 7.15 and 8.00. The mean, mode, and median were 7.70, 7.55 and 7.75, and 7.60. "Eighty per cent of the specimens were above pH 7.25 and below 7.95." (196:409.)

In a later study, Starr (197) reports a corroboration of his original results and stresses that stutterers have characteristic high alveolar carbon dioxide as opposed to non-stutterers. He postulates that this is due to a relative insensitivity of the respiratory center resulting in an oxygen deficiency and probable pathological increase of the toxins in the blood. He believes that a decrease in the carbohydrate content of the diet and the introduction of proper breathing exercises in the open air would prove of benefit to the stutterer.

Kopp (131), in a series of carefully controlled laboratory experiments involving blood analyses from the basilic and cephalic veins, discovered that certain chemical entities are found in the blood of stutterers in proportions different from the established ratios. His experiments were based upon control groups and upon groups of stutterers ranging from 11 in number (8 males; 3 females) to 23 in number (16 males; 7 females). Except for one experiment (i.e., serum calcium experiment in which the ages of the stutterers ranged from 6 to 39 years), all experimental groups of stutterers ranged from 20 to 39 years of age.

Perhaps the most significant differences that Kopp demonstrated are: (1) stutterers' *globulin* is 22.7 per cent lower than normals' with a probability of a real difference in 100 chances out of 100; (2) stutterers' *sugar* is 17.4 per cent higher than normals' with a probability of a real difference in 100 chances out of 100; (3) stutterers' *inorganic phosphate* is 14.8 per cent higher than normals' with 99 chances out of 100 that a true difference exists; (4) stutterers' *total protein* is 12.6 per cent lower than normals' with 99 chances out of 100 of a real difference; (5) stutterers' total *serum calcium* is 5.59 per cent higher than normals' with 99 chances out of 100 of a true difference; (6) stutterers' *non-diffusible* is 10.4 per cent higher than normals' with 99 chances out of 100 that there is a true difference; (7) stutterers' *potassium* is 6.63 per cent lower than normals' with 95 chances out of 100 of a true difference; (8) stutterers' *albumin* is 8.85 per cent lower than normals' with 92 chances out of 100 that a true difference exists.

Slight, but statistically insignificant, differences are reported for other substances, such as *non-protein nitrogen,* diffusible *calcium, cholesterol,* and *chlorides* (131:121).

In plotting the various data, Kopp found that the blood pattern of the stutterer, as shown by the correlations of total serum calcium, potassium, inorganic phosphate, total protein, and non-protein nitrogen, is practically the reverse of the blood pattern of the non-stutterers (131:129-130). Hence, his conclusion that stuttering is a manifestation of disturbed metabolism.

The results of these independent studies may be viewed to be highly corroborative of each other. Of notable significance, seem to be the following: Trumper's finding of a high erythrocyte count in the stutterers' blood, probably the result of sympathetic stimulation of the spleen; Starr's discovery of the high pH content of stutterers' saliva; and Kopp's demonstration of stutterers' high blood sugar—all of which may be interpreted as biochemical components of emotionality. In passing, it is also interesting to draw attention to the connection that may exist between Kopp's result that stutterers' total protein is lower than non-stutterers' and Dunlap's study (65) of stutterers' case histories in which he found: (1) many stutterers to have had little or no meat in their childhood; and (2) large numbers of adolescent stutterers to be vegetarians.

Stutterers have characteristic vasomotor conditions

Robbins (177) experimented with 10 stutterers and 13 college seniors and graduate students as controls to determine whether the changes in the blood volume in either right hand or second finger of the right hand revealed characteristic differences between the two groups. He used a plethysmograph to measure the blood volume of both groups in various situations, such as during speech, during silence, during emotional reactions which he stimulated, etc. His results indicate significant differences, especially in that stammerers experience greater and more rapid vaso-constriction and slower recovery from emotional stimuli than do normal speakers.

Palmer and Gillett (163) conducted an experiment in which they recorded the pulse rate of 24 stutterers and 28 non-stutterers by means of the Lombard radial pulse apparatus. "Significant differences were immediately recognized between the results for age level, sex, normals, and stutterers, not only in the mean pulse rates, but in the standard deviations." (163:7.) No difference was accepted as significant below a *t* of 3.00. All stutterers have less regular pulse rates than all normals (163:10). In the case of male stutterers between the ages of 18 and 26 years, there is significantly more irregular pulse rates than their controls (163:11). Pulse rhythms of normal subjects decrease in irregularity as age increases. However, stutterers' cardiac rhythms increase in irregularity. While this is true of stutterers of both sexes, male stutterers reveal a significantly larger increase in irregularity.

The results of these experiments confirm those of Trumper, Starr, Kopp, and others reported on pages 32-36.

Stutterers have characteristic tremor rates

Travis has stated: "It may be observed that the fingers when extended present small rhythmical movements or tremors which occur at a rate ranging from 8 to 12 per second." (229:152.) Following this cue, Herren experimented with a group of stutterers and a group of non-stutterers acting as controls. Two results of his experiment were significant: he found that the stutterers as a group, during the act of stuttering, depressed their tremors and that in voluntary effort the stutterers frequently and the normal speakers infrequently gave a tremor rate ranging from 40 to 75 tremors per second (109).

Voluntary movements of stutterers are atypical

In a subsequent experiment, Herren had the subjects of both experimental and control groups grasp a rubber bulb in each hand and in phase alternately flex and extend the fingers of the two hands. The movements were recorded on a smoked drum. He discovered that stuttering speech among male stutterers ranging in age from 20 to 25 years produced complete inhibition in the voluntary movements described. The reduction in the extent of the movements corresponded to the length and severity of the stuttering. This disturbance appeared in both hands, in only one hand when both were being used, or in either hand when it was used singly. These phenomena did not occur in the controls. "All these disturbances occurred at the time of the tonic or clonic speech blocks." (109:298.)

West (247) constructed a neurological test for stutterers on the basis of his discovery that stutterers were significantly slower in the rate of repetitive, voluntary movements of the mandible and supercilious muscles, i.e., above the eyebrows.

Blackburn (24) studied the voluntary movements of diaphragm, tongue, lips, and jaw in stutterers and normal speakers. His results indicate that stutterers are inferior to non-stutterers in the control of the simple voluntary rhythmical movements of these organs in at least two specific ways: stutterers differ distinctly from normal speakers in the regularity and in the rate of movement of the four speech structures considered. The differences between the experimental and control groups were especially marked in the case of the diaphragm and tongue.

Hunsley's study (114) of 20 mature stutterers, 17 men and 3 women, concerning the speech musculature of stutterers is also corroborative. He required the stutterers—and the controls—to produce with each of the muscle groups, i.e., jaws, lips, and tongue, in turn a temporal pattern of clicks from an auditory stimulation pattern. His statistical analysis of the results reveals significant differences: stutterers were inferior to the controls in their ability to perform a silent pattern of movement in time with the speech musculature (114:49).

Bills (23) wished to determine what relationships, if any, existed between stuttering and fatigue. He experimented with 26 male and 2 female stutterers of college age and with a control group of 33 non-stutterers of like age. Two records, i.e., vocal and manual, were kept of the subjects while they named colors from the Woodworth-Wells Color Charts. Among the significant results, Bills emphasizes that (1) stutterers show a 20 per cent increase in length blocks in manual performance, and a 25 per cent increase in vocal blocks (23:579); (2) the blocking frequency shows a relatively large increase in the case of normals and almost no increase with the stutterers. Stuttering symptoms are seemingly not aggravated by fatigue whereas fatigue apparently produces speech blocks in non-stutterers (23:580).

Several experimenters have studied voluntary muscular movements among stutterers. Their results are uniform in that they identify the stutterer as inferior to the non-stutterer in the control of simple voluntary rhythmical movements of such organs as the diaphragm, tongue, lips, mandible, and eyebrows. That stutterers find difficulty in voluntarily controlling musculatures in non-speaking activities and non-stutterers do not is further evidence of fundamental differences between the two groups.

Stutterers differ from non-stutterers in breathing actions

The evidence that stutterers differ from non-stutterers in breathing is conclusive. The findings of early experimenters, Halle (103), Ten Cate (216), Gutzmann (101), and others have been corroborated and extended by present-day experimentalists, Fletcher (73), Fossler (76), Murray (157), Travis (227), et al. Among the findings, the following differences are especially pertinent.

Stutterers attempt to speak on inspiration; normal speakers do not. Among the first experimentalists to describe this phenomenon was Halle (103), and it has been corroborated by Fossler (76) and Travis (227).

The breathing of stutterers during speech is marked by arhythm; the breathing of normal speaking is marked by rhythmic control. Gutzmann (101), Fletcher (73), Bryngelson (42) and Travis (227) have presented objective evidence attesting that stutterers protract inspiration and expiration markedly during speech, whereas non-stutterers do not. Secondly, stutterers as contrasted to non-stutterers show pathologic variability and inequality in the extent of consecutive respiratory movements during speech. Thirdly, the breathing of stutterers during speech is marked by interruptions of expiratory by short inspiratory movements whereas normal speakers do not show this type of disintegration.

The breathing of stutterers during speech is marked by horizontal disintegration; the breathing of non-stutterers is bi-laterally unified. Vera Travis (233) reports that during speaking in the case of normal speakers the two halves of the diaphragmatic breathing mechanism function as a unit. In her study of the breathing of 41 stutterers during speech, 90 per cent of the stutterers showed horizontal (diaphragmatic) disintegration.

Stutterers reveal disintegration of the breathing mechanism during rest breathing; non-stutterers do not. Murray studied the rest breathing of 18 college stutterers and 18 controls during silent reading by the use of the kymograph. He found that stutterers (1) repressed the amplitude of their breathing by an average of 121 per cent more than non-stutterers; (2) revealed 51 per cent greater variability in duration of inspiration and 112.3 per cent greater variability on the average duration of expiration. As the difficulty of reading materials increased the disintegration of the rest breathing was much more rapid and pronounced in the stutterers. In his summary, Murray states: "In all phases of the breathing, stutterers showed approximately two-thirds as much variability during silent reading as other experimenters have shown them to present during overt speech." (157:242.)

Stutterers reveal periodic breath pressure during speech; non-stutterers do not. Travis reports that "A periodic fluctuation in breath pressure is evident in photographic records of the stutterer's speech just before and immediately after tones. These waves occur at a rate varying from

25 to 50 per second both during stuttering and when there are no observable signs of difficulty in speaking. However, they rarely if ever occur in the speech of the normal speaker." (228:657.)

Stutterers have characteristic reflexive movements.

Travis and Dorsey studied the patellar reflex time of stutterers and non-stutterers. They found that "during a tonic block the patellar-tendon reflex time is significantly reduced in the majority of stutterers. Speech of the normal speaker has no appreciable effect upon the reflex time." (231:149.)

Gardner (86) experimented with 17 stutterers of college age and a control group of like age in reference to the pupillary light reflex. He discovered that the normal pupillary response to light was consistently altered in dilated diameter during spasms of stuttering. This did not take place during the speech of the normal speakers.

While it is impossible to say that stutterers differ from non-stutterers in reflexive movements generally, in the two experiments that have been performed, significant differences are demonstrated in two reflexes.

Stutterers have characteristic vocal anomalies

Travis made a phono-photographic study of the voices of 19 stutterers and 18 non-stutterers. His conclusions indicate that stutterers and non-stutterers differ in regard to the tonal effect of emotional situations upon voice. Stutterers have less variability in the pitch of a sustained tone after an emotional upheaval than under normal circumstances, while non-stutterers have more variability in the pitch of a sustained tone after an emotional upset than under ordinary conditions. "Thus, in the case of the stutterer, emotion decreases the flexibility of the voice while in the case of the non-stutterer it increases the flexibility of the voice." (230:1041.)

Bryngelson (42), using similar techniques to Travis', analyzed the phono-photographic records of 17 stutterers and 9 non-stutterers. Unlike the non-stutterers, the stutterers' films showed: (1) marked variations in the form, length, and intensity of consecutive sound waves; (2) extreme tonal rigidity; (3) a variety of isolated waves; (4) a variety of abnormal attacks on tones; (5) a variety of abnormal endings on tones; (6) a form of vocalization on inhalation; (7) informative sucking and snoring noises; and (8) pulsations in the breath stream before, between, and after tones. Another revealing difference was that stutterers' attempts to change real stuttering into voluntary stuttering produced imitative movements that showed all the vocal phenomena of stuttering, whereas the non-stutterers were unable to simulate vocal stuttering symptoms.

Stutterers reveal significant differences from non-stutterers in regard to eye movements

Murray (157) experimented with 18 college stutterers and 18 college controls to determine, among other questions, whether stutterers have characteristic eye movements during silent reading and reasoning. He administered reading matter of increasing difficulty to both groups. The results of his experiment reveal in regard to a quantitative evaluation of the data that (1) stutterers had an average of 22.34 per cent more fixations per line than non-stutterers and 126.5 per cent more regressive movements; (2) the average duration of fixations was 10.3 per cent longer for stutterers than for the controls; (3) the average perception time per line was 4.09 per cent longer in duration for stutterers; (4) the variability of the duration of fixations was 44.52 per cent greater for stutterers.

A qualitative analysis of the eye-movement patterns resulted in the following conclusions: (1) 49.74 per cent of the eye-movement patterns over the lines of reading matter of the stutterers followed as few as two typical patterns of movement whereas 76.27 per cent of the movements made by the non-stutterers followed only two typical patterns.

Stutterers compare unfavorably to non-stutterers in tests of motor co-ordination

Westphal (252) studied certain motor abilities of 26 male stutterers ranging in age from 8 to 17 years and a control group of like ages and sex. The instruments employed were: (1) The Smedley Dynamometer to measure hand grip; (2) a bead tossing test; (3) The Goddard-Norsworthy arrangement of the Sequin Board (choice of hands was observed on the first trial—for the second and third trials the subject was instructed which hand to use); (4) simultaneous writing of digits with both hands was administered while the subjects were blindfolded and the time and number of reversals were recorded; (5) The Stoelting Nine-Hole Steadiness Plate was used with the subjects alternating hands; (6) height and weight measurements were taken.

The results of the study indicate that the non-stutterers as a group made scores that are better than those for stutterers. The non-stutterers were heavier, stronger with the right and left hand, and had better eye-hand co-ordination in all of the functions. Westphal concludes the report of the study with these words: "There is no instance in which stutterers as a group are better than non-stutterers with the possible exception of the Stoelting Plate data. It must be pointed out that the data on the Stoelting Plate for holes eight and nine may be spurious." (252:221.)

In a later study, Cross (58) experimented with 21 male stutterers of college and university ages. She used a control group of 31 right-handed and 11 left-handed normal speakers. She administered the Stanford Motor Skills Tests, viz., Koerth Pursuit Rotor, Motor Rhythm, Serial Discrimeter, Brown Spool Packer, Speed of Tapping Test.

Significant differences between the two groups were revealed: (1) stutterers were significantly inferior to normals in bimanual activity; (2) stutterers were significantly inferior to normals in the rate of movement of the right hand and the left hand; (3) stutterers showed more similarity between the two hands or more ambidexterity than normal speakers.

All these experiments and studies pertaining to morphological differences between stutterers and non-stutterers may be supplemented by a consideration of researches in that field of personality widely known as mental abilities and capacities.

CHAPTER V

Personality Structure of Stutterers: Mental Capacities

While the experiments and studies of stutterers relating to that aspect of personality here identified as mental abilities and capacities have not been as numerous as in other aspects, the evidence is impressive.

Perseveration is greater among stutterers than non-stutterers

Woodworth (258:91) defines perseveration as "A recent activity that reasserts itself, without any apparent cue or stimulus to arouse it . . ." He also states that "some persons are much more subject to it than others." A similar definition is given by Bonnet (37:52), who describes perseveration as a sort of physiological inertia, by reason of which in a complicated series of functions involving muscular coordinations, if one of these acts cannot be executed, through any form of inhibition, the preceding one will continue to function until the inhibited act takes place.

In studying the perseveration tendency in stutterers, Eisenson and Pastel (68) experimented with 30 male stutterers ranging in age from 10 to 15 years of age with a control group of like number. A group of tests in the Mahler-Elkin Test was used in which (1) a situation is presented to which the subject is required to respond for a given period of time (Pre-test A); (2) a variation of this situation is then presented to which the subject is required to make a different response for the same period (Pre-test B); (3) a third situation, consisting of the combination in random order of both original situations, is then presented.

The subject is here required to change his reactions quickly and suddenly. A failure means that the subject continued to react to a situation which was no longer present. It is statistically significant that the difference of the mean scores was 2.7 which was interpreted to mean that (1) stutterers perseverate more than non-stutterers, and (2) "The perseveration is an indication of a resistance to change and lack of adaptability of the stutterers." (68:631.) These results become even more significant when they are linked to those of Pinard (168) who found that perseverators tend to be nervous and sensitive.

Intelligence of stutterers

With a cursory reading of the literature on stuttering one discovers statements such as: "Stutterers are more numerous among the mentally retarded," or "Stutterers have been noticed to be exceptionally intelligent," or "Stutterers are normal in intelligence," and the like. A more intensive study reveals that there is a growing body of evidence indicating that stutterers are not subnormal in intelligence, and perhaps they are somewhat more intelligent than non-stutterers. This conclusion seems warranted after reviewing the latest research into this field.

Speech defects among idiots

Kennedy (126) observed the speech of 500 idiots and selected from that number 32 whom the investigator made certain were typical of the idiot population. The subjects ranged in chronological age from 7 years, 9 months to 38 years and in intelligence quotient up to 20. Their speech varied from a mechanically accurate, though entirely irrelevant speech, to absolute mutism. Although many types of dyslalias (articulatory disorders) that are found among all ranges of intelligence were noticed among the idiots, no cases of stuttering were recorded. We have here what might be called a piece of negative evidence attesting to the higher intelligence distribution of stutterers.

Stuttering among people of high intelligence

At the opposite end of the scale, Havelock Ellis (70) found a large number of stutterers among persons of high ability and accomplishment. He has this to say: "Among the minor forms of nervous derangement stammering is of great significance. I have ascertained that at least 13 of the eminent persons on my list (12 men and one woman) stammered. These are Bagehot (?), R. Boyle, Curran, Croker, Erasmus Darwin, Dodgson, Mrs. Inchbald, C. Kingsley, Lamb, Magin, Priestly, Sheil, Sidgwick. Seven others are noted as having defects of speech which are sometimes stated not to amount to a stammer, but in other cases were doubtless ordinary stammering. When it is remembered that the normal occurrence of stammering or stuttering among adults is below one per cent and also that my record is certainly very incomplete, it will be seen that there can be no doubt whatever as to the abnormal prevalence of stammering among British persons of ability." Here again is a piece of evidence indicating a skewness toward high intelligence in the case of stutterers.

Intelligence of stuttering children

In the studies compiled by West, Travis, and Camp for the White House Conference of 1930, they found that the median I.Q. for stutterers was 96.5 in a group of 4059 stutterers. This median I.Q. was higher than the median I.Q. found for children having structural-articulatory defects, for those having organic speech defects, for those having oral inaccuracies. Another result reported was that stutterers are not mentally retarded (254:320-321).

Travis (229) studied the distribution of intelligence quotients of stuttering children reported by the Child Guidance Department of Madison, Wisconsin, and found that the intelligence quotients were not only symmetrically distributed but that 98 per cent of the cases were above 69 I.Q. McDowell administered the Binet Intelligence Test to 61 stuttering children and compared their results with the norms of the tests. She found the stuttering group "Practically typical." When she compared the results of the group on the Pintner-Patterson Non-Language Intelligence Test with results of a control group, she found the stutterers better than the controls by 4.4 points, although the variation of the two groups was large (149).

The intelligence of college stutterers

The evidence concerning the intelligence of college stutterers is quite uniform: that college stutterers are superior in intelligence to college non-stutterers. The college stutterers in Johnson's study ranged in I.Q. from 105 to 136. He states: "The college stutterers were definitely of superior intelligence." (120:19.)

Steer, who experimented with 87 college stutterers, found the average I.Q. to be 116.5. He states that 6.8 per cent ranged below 99 I.Q.; one per cent between 110 I.Q. and 133 I.Q. The range was found to be from 80 I.Q. to 139 I.Q. The median normal was 111 I.Q., which in the case of stutterers was 118 I.Q. Eighty per cent of the intelligence quotients were at the normal median or above. By percentile, with 50 normal, in percentile standings the stutterers rate 69 (199:864).

When it is recalled that the incidence of stuttering is from two to three times greater at the college level than at lower educational levels or among the total population (compare Tables 1 and 2), the results of Steer's and Johnson's studies take on added significance.

Stutterers are less efficient silent readers than non-stutterers

In normal reading, the principle of rhythm has been well established by the studies of Buswell (47), Dearborn

(62), Gates (88, 89), C. T. Gray (95), W. S. Gray (97), Robinson (180), and others. Then, too, Travis (228), Jasper and Murray (117), and others have demonstrated that stutterers are afflicted with disintegration of eye movements, especially during speech and silent reading activities. Hence, it is reasonable to assume that a group of stutterers matched with a group of non-stutterers for age, intelligence, etc., will make lower scores on silent reading tests. This assumption has been confirmed. Murray (157) discovered, as a result of testing 18 college stutterers and 18 non-stuttering controls, that the stuttering group was one grade below the normals in comprehension of reading matter and two grades below the normals in rate of silent reading. Similar conclusions are reached by Kelley (123).

Stutterers differ from non-stutterers in mirror reading ability

Peters (167) investigated the question as to whether facility in mirror reading is related to the functions of speech and reading. He examined 100 junior and senior high school students, and found that 25 were stutterers. Using these 25 stutterers and two control groups, one of 25 normal right-handed students, the other of 25 normal left-handed students matched for age and intelligence, he submitted the three groups to the same battery of tests. He found that the critical ratios of the difference between the group means were: 3.07 for stutterers and right-handed normals; 2.0 for stutterers and left-handed normals. This leaves practically no doubt that stutterers possess a genuine superiority over right-handed normal speakers with regard to facility in mirror reading. This superiority is further indicated by the result that of the 25 subjects making the best mirror reading scores (upper quartile), 40 per cent were stutterers; and the 25 per cent subjects making the poorest scores (lowest quartile) included only 4 per cent of the stutterers.

Stutterers differ from non-stutterers in written language ability

Eisenson (69) posed the question: Does the stutterer carry over into his written language the characteristics which are manifest in his spoken language? In order to answer the question, he used a group of 15 college, male stutterers and a control group of equal number matched for age and class. Both groups were asked to write for fifteen minutes on a subject that was being widely discussed in the college where the experiment took place. The number of words written was taken as a measure of "talkativeness," and the number of words crossed out was taken as an indication of "verbal trial and error." He found that the mean number of words written by stutterers was half that written by the non-stuttering group. In regard to the number of words crossed out the difference between the mean and the two groups as measured by the formula $\dfrac{\text{difference}}{\sigma \text{ difference}}$ is 6.7, "indicating unquestionable statistical significance" in favor of the stutterers (69:458). The conclusions drawn from this study indicate that stutterers are less talkative than non-stutterers in terms of written language, and stutterers' language is more marked by trial and error.

Stutterers are more facile at mirror writing than non-stutterers

In summarizing the research on mirror writing, Blom (30) concludes that it is as normal for left-handed people as is the conventional writing for right-handed people. Fagan (71) and Travis (225) have both found that stutterers more frequently than non-stutterers reveal mirror writing tendencies and that stutterers are better mirror writers than non-stutterers.

Relationships between stuttering and handedness

The facility which stutterers manifest with respect to mirror reading and mirror writing brings up the question of handedness, or, to use a more comprehensive term, sidedness. Many studies concerning sidedness, its causes, its incidence, and the like, have been made. On the one hand, there are many studies whose results indicate a close relationship between sinistrality or ambilaterality and stuttering. On the other hand, there are studies like those of Wallin (239) and Parsons (165) whose results indicate that the vast majority of left-handed children who had been forced to write with the right hand did not develop stuttering, or in the few cases that did develop stuttering it disappeared after the change of handedness had been completed.

One study of the former group is pertinent here because it deals with college stutterers and control groups of college non-stutterers. After selecting groups on the basis of a handedness questionnaire, Van Riper (237) administered the Van Riper Quantitative Test of Laterality to 35 thoroughly right-handed non-stutterers, 35 thoroughly left-handed non-stutterers, and 30 stutterers. He found that the results of the stuttering group were significantly similar to the results of the ambidexterous group and significantly dissimilar to the right-handed group.

Travis, in summarizing the pros and cons of the question of laterality and stuttering, concludes that "The most careful laboratory studies show a sinistral or ambilateral nature to be characteristic of . . . most stutterers. However, all studies, including the laboratory ones, demonstrate a significant minority of stutterers to be strictly dextral. . ." (228:695.)

CHAPTER VI

Need of Studying the Personality Structure of Stutterers
in Regard to Temperament

Despite the widespread interest in the relationship between stuttering and personality traits, the studies in this
field are few and the results are inconclusive.

Emotional adjustments of stuttering children

McDowell (149) studied children showing varying degrees of the severity of stuttering cramps by the equivalent-
group method. She administered all of the following personality tests and the examinations to 46 pairs of children:
(1) Woodworth-Matthews Questionnaire; (2) Woodworth-
Cady Questionnaire; (3) Kent-Rosanoff Free Association
Test.

No significant differences between the groups were
found in the result of the Woodworth, Cady, Matthews
Questionnaires. As for the results of the Kent-Rosanoff
Association Test, there was "No significant difference . . .
either in reaction times or in the quality of the responses."
(149:49.)

It is doubtful whether these results, among the first in
this field, may be accepted as conclusive, for a number
of reasons. The populations studied were small—46 pairs.
The stutterers, although all elementary school children,
were not all of the same age or grade. The experimental
group, identified and selected as stutterers by McDowell,
"showed varied degrees of the severity of the stuttering
cramps." (149:14.) In a critical light, two questions seem
pertinent: What were the degrees of the severity? Would

other speech specialists agree to her criteria of severity? Then, too, authorities report lower reliabilities for children's results on personality questionnaires than adults'. Symonds, in reviewing the reliability coefficients of personality questionnaires in studies involving children as subjects, explains the relatively low coefficients thus: (1) "adults are better able to introspect; (2) personal experience, characteristics, etc., being better developed in adults than in children, stand out more clearly and are thus easier to distinguish; (3) many questionnaires—because of vocabularies used—are beyond the comprehension of children." (213:164-167.) Then, too, the administration of the tests was admittedly faulty. Instead of replying to the items on the questionnaires as demanded by the directions, the children were invited to respond orally at the length as they wished. McDowell writes: "The technique of testing is known to be at fault in certain instances and was probably at fault in certain others." Still another consideration involves the use of the Kent-Rosanoff Free Association Test in this study. Because the response time to the stimulus words is of fundamental importance in the interpretation of the results of this test, its use for the purposes of study, with stutterers—on account of the very nature of their speech blocks—is of doubtful value.

Personality problems of college stutterers

Johnson (120) studied the personality problems of 80 stutterers, male and female, ranging in age from 7 to 42 years. Twenty-five of these subjects scored 22 or above (maladjusted) on the Maturity section of the Woodworth-House Mental Hygiene Inventory and 25 of these scored 21 or below (well-adjusted) on the Maturity section. He found that "in maturity the stutterers had significantly more extreme problems than did House's normals." (120:88.) The items which differentiate between stutterers and House's normals were: "Stutterers reveal more poor health, nervousness and irritability, shyness, vocational anxiety, secretiveness and depression, belief of being unsatisfactorily adjusted to life." (120:88.)

Although Johnson states that "Apparently stuttering becomes, with increasing age, a greater and greater burden with which non-stutterers do not have to contend, but which renders the adjustments of stutterers more difficult," his study does not adequately answer the questions: Do college, male stutterers have more disturbances of temperament than non-stutterers? Are college, male stutterers afflicted characteristically with peculiarities of temperament? First of all the population of the experimental group was small. Stutterers of varying ages were used, only 19 of the group being of college or university level. Stutterers of varying degree of severity of stuttering were used. Likewise stutterers of varying intelligence and educational achievement were used. Finally, House's norms were used rather than those based on a control group.

Discussion of the disparity of results between McDowell's and Johnson's studies

Assuming that the shortcomings of both these studies did not affect the reliability and validity of the results, how can the disparity in the findings be accounted for? Bluemel's theory of primary and secondary stuttering may well be the answer. According to Bluemel (33) primary stuttering denotes the gross symptoms of disordered speech marked by tonic and clonic spasms especially in early childhood. Psychologically it is marked by unawareness on the part of the afflicted child of the social discomforts of hesitant speech. Secondary stuttering, on the other hand, is rarely identified as such until after the child leaves home to enter new and strange societies, such as the school. In addition to the symptoms of primary stuttering, secondary stuttering is marked by the child's realization that his speech handicap entails feelings of unpleasantness in social situations.

In other words, primary stuttering is the speech handicap itself while secondary stuttering is the reaction, i.e., mental attitudes, of the stutterer to his speech handicap. Thus, the older stuttering child is likely to be afflicted with secondary symptoms because of the demand of fluency in most socialized speech situations.

This concept of primary and secondary stuttering may be used logically to explain the results of investigations that reveal the incidence of stuttering to be greater in childhood than in adolescence or maturity. For instance, Milisen and Johnson (154) found that "40 per cent of stuttering was outgrown" mostly before the school life of the child began. Steer (201) has discovered similar results. Ostensibly, the conditions causing stuttering in such cases disappear before the causes of secondary stuttering are met.

As in the case of the disparity between McDowell's and Johnson's results, the concept also serves as a reasonable explanation of other disparate results. An example is found in the studies of Eisenson and Meltzer. The former found post-pubertal male stutterers to be less "talkative" and given to more trial and error in written language than a like group of non-stutterers. Meltzer (152), who experimented with pre-pubertal stutterers by using the Rorschach Personality Test,* discovered that stutterers were more "talkative" and given to more trial and error than like non-stutterers. Assuming that both researchers identified the same entity by their respective definitions of "talkativeness" and "trial and error," might not the contradiction of their results be due to the differences of the age of the groups studied? From this point of view, it may

---

* Composed of a series of large cards on which are vague and cloudy smears. These smears or blots are interpreted in individual and frequently revealing ways by the subject when he is asked, "What might this be?"

be maintained that male stutterers before and after puberty reveal a greater tendency toward verbal trial and error than non-stutterers and that pre-pubertal stutterers show more "talkativeness" than non-stutterers of the same developmental age and post-pubertal stutterers show less "talkativeness" than non-stutterers of like developmental age.

SUMMARY

Whatever explanation is finally corroborated, the need is apparent to describe and to define the temperament or personality traits of stutterers at the various chronological and developmental ages.

To date, the large majority of all objective studies in the field of stuttering deals with post-pubertal male stutterers. At this age, the evidence strongly indicates that male stutterers differ from male non-stutterers in certain aspects of morphology and mental capacity. Adequate studies pertaining to the temperament or personality traits of post-pubertal male stutterers are lacking.

An experiment to determine whether college, male stutterers have personality traits that set them apart as a group

1. Do college, male stutterers have more disturbances of temperament or personality traits than non-stutterers?

2. Are college, male stutterers afflicted characteristically with certain specific peculiarities of personality?

Because answers to these questions might have important implications, it was decided to set up an experiment to attempt to answer them. Such an experiment, based on personality tests, would involve certain precautionary measures:

1. Large numbers of college, male stutterers with comparable symptoms of stuttering would have to be used in the experiment.

2. Personality tests used in the experiment would be

selected on the basis of optimum reliability and validity.

3. The tests would be administered to comparable groups of non-stutterers matched with stutterers in as many ways as possible.

Before embarking upon such an experiment, however, it was necessary to select an instrument and to evaluate it.

Chapter VII

The Personality Inventory as a Means of Studying
Personality Traits of Temperament

I. *The History of Instruments for the Measurement of
Personality Traits*

The history of instruments* of the questionnaire type
for the study of personality traits begins in 1917 when
Woodworth set about to find a method of diagnosing the
ability of men to adjust themselves to the emotional strains
of army life. His study resulted in a *Personal Data Sheet*
or the *Woodworth Psychoneurotic Inventory*. It is composed of 116 questions which are answered by *yes* or *no*.
The 116 questions have been roughly classified by
Symonds as "physical symptoms, pains, weariness, inco-
ordinations; adjustment with the environment; fears;
worries, unhappiness, unsocial and anti-social moods and
conduct; dreams, phantasies, sleep disturbances; reactions
to drink, tobacco, drugs, sex; mental symptoms; vacilla-
tions; compulsions; questions about one's family."
(213:178.)

Most of the subsequent investigators in this field have
utilized Woodworth's items. Matthews (147) first and Cady
(48) a few years later adapted them—dropping some and
adding others—for children. They were both interested in
identifying those children who had difficulty in making
adjustment to the home and school. Matthews' questionnaire was used to study 1113 unselected children of both
sexes from 9 to 19 years of age. She also used it in making

---

* The most common names of personality trait-tests or tests of temperament are: questionnaires, inventories, adjustment blanks, etc.

a study of a smaller number of children with abnormal emotional and character traits. Travis (229:88) has classified the subject matter of Matthews' questions into the following groups.

1. Fears, worries, etc.: 21 questions.

2. Physical symptoms, pains, weariness, inco-ordinations: 25 questions.

3. Unhappiness, unsocial and anti-social moods: 37 questions.

4. Dreams, phantasies, sleep disturbances: 16 questions.

Symonds' questionnaire for adolescents (215) concerns especially "school adjustment situations."

Although House's inventory (113) is designed for the college level, it directs a number of the questions to experiences occurring before the age of 14 years. His object was to meet the contention of the psychoanalyst that maladjustment in later life has its origins in inimical childhood experiences. There are 100 problems in this inventory which the individual is required to check on the basis of whether or not these problems have occurred in his life. Under a childhood period, the upper limit of which is placed at 14, there are 30 problems listed. Seventy problems are allocated to the mature period, which is any time after 14.

At Colgate University, Laird (135) experimented with the Woodworth Inventory, and he evolved his own *Personality Inventory*. His adaptations are notable for two developments. First of all, he substituted a graphic rating scale on each answer for the *yes* or *no* response. Secondly, he so grouped the questions as to make finer distinctions possible. Those distinctions he called "psychasthenoid," "schizoid," "neurasthenoid," and "hysteroid." They serve as descriptions of the various degrees on the linear scale.

Another inventory which took especial cognizance of the insight gained by psychoanalysis was the *Experience*

Variables Record of Chassell (50). He used the rating idea and described degrees of presence or absence of the variables involved, and emphasized the situation in which the maladjustment occurs rather than the kind of response alone. Data concerning childhood experiences were also included. The following sections are descriptive of the types of situations that were included: mother relationships; father relationships; relationships with brothers and sisters; family life; religion and standards; sex developments; love affairs—crushes and heterosexual adjustments; physical development; intellectual development; vocational adjustment; social situation—adjustment in comrade groups, status in community, public recognition; general emotional adjustment, happiness, etc.

One of the most elaborate of the inventories is Allport's *Systematic Questionnaire for the Study of Personality*. It covers the following ten fields of inquiry: (1) development, (2) intelligence, (3) emotion and bodily activity, (4) ambitions, interests, and vocational tendencies, (5) habits of work, (6) recreation, (7) character, (8) sex family life, (9) attitude, (10) compensation and self-improvement. The subject is asked to take note of his behavior for a week after reading the questionnaire through several times. At the end of the week he answers the questionnaire to the best of his ability. Further, he is asked to give the questionnaire to a friend and obtain his estimation of the subjects in relation to the same questions. The final step is taken up by the subject when he makes a comparison between his answers and those of his friend. He, of course, takes especial care in noting any discrepancies and makes an introspective study of himself in the items where disagreement occurs.

In 1930 the Thurstones published their *Personality Inventory* of 223 questions which were compiled from the instruments of Woodworth, House, Laird, Freyd, Allport. The questions may be answered by *yes, no, ?*. The score is the number of questions answered the way emotionally maladjusted individuals have been found to answer. The questions were standardized upon 694 University of Chicago freshmen. One of the most interesting results that the Thurstones found was that neurotic students were better students than their well-adjusted classmates. Because the Thurstone Personality Inventory has a high degree of reliability and because it is standardized for women as well as for men, it has been used widely.

Jung's theory of psychological types has had a significant influence on the development of a somewhat different type of adjustment questionnaire which is concerned with the measurement of introversion-extroversion. Freyd's list of diagnostic items together with the investigations of Heidbreder (107), Marston (145), and Laird (135), represents the belief that instruments can be constructed of the tendency of an individual to respond definitely in either one of two directions: introvertedly, or extrovertedly. As a matter of fact, these investigators found that people distributed themselves along the normal curve of distribution (Gaussian Curve), with the greatest number in the middle of the scale—that is, between the poles of introversion and extroversion. Hence, a third term has come into use—ambiversion. The present procedure in measurement describes a person as tending toward introversion or extroversion in his response to a given situation.

Freyd's list (79) contains 54 characteristics of introversion, and upon these Heidbreder (107) based her inventory. Heidbreder employs +, −, ? for denoting the presence, absence, or neutral position of the characteristic in the individual. Form C-2 (for the subject) and Form C-3 (for the subject's friends) of the Colgate Personality Inventory by Laird (135) have been used abundantly for measuring traits of introversion and extroversion. Interest questionnaires, performance tests, and free-association tests have been used in measuring introversion and extroversion tendencies, but not to the extent of the personality questionnaire or inventory.

Another type of personality test that is of interest here is the ascendance-submission scale best represented by Allport's (5) test. The Allport Test appears in two forms; one for men, the other for women. The test is composed of a list of questions which concern situations in which people are said to react in an ascendant or submissive manner. The subject is asked to rate himself on the kind of response he is likely to make. There are three ways provided for answering each question—"Habitually," "Occasionally," "Never."

The Pressey X-O tests have been found valuable for studying the emotional background of the subject. The tests are really lists of words which the individual is given to read. Those words, which are interpreted as unpleasant, sinful, or worrying, or which are in any way associated in his mind with a key word, are crossed out. There have been several adaptations of the Pressey Tests, one of the latest being the Davis Personal Reaction Sheet. On it the subject is asked to indicate the degree of feeling that he associates with the given words. Numbers ranging from 5 to 25 are used, 25 being the number that represents the greatest intensity of feeling.

One of the newest personality tests, and one that has been widely adopted both in research work and in diagnosis, is the *Bernreuter Personality Inventory* (20). Bernreuter compiled his inventory from the questions and data found in the instrument of the Thurstones, Woodworth, House, Laird, Freyd, Allport, Oliver, Conklin, Strong, Pressey, Whitman, and Bernreuter. At the present, it provides for 6 separate measures of personality traits on the basis of the same 125 items. These traits are neurotic tendency, dominance-submission, introversion-extroversion, self-sufficiency-dependency, confidence-in-oneself, sociability.

II. *Criticisms Lodged against the Personality Inventory*

As personality inventories have increased in number and use, psychologists have accepted them with varying degrees of enthusiasm. To a large extent, the type of endorsement and criticism directed to personality inventories by psychologists can be traced to their philosophies. Some of the most frequently mentioned criticisms are the following:

1. *The very construction of the inventory is likely to be faulty.*

"Even if we set up and standardize sample situations for a test, the very fact of their experimental nature may defeat our whole purpose. If, as has often been attempted, our set-up is a problem situation on paper, the situation is hypothetical instead of actual, and the answer of the individual taking the test is likely to be hypothetical instead of actual also. . . A person may know the correct thing to do and so express it on a paper-and-pencil test, but fail to act accordingly in the actual situation." Hunt (115:323).

2. *The personality inventory, which doubtless samples a variety of traits and tendencies, often pretends to measure a generalized trait.*

"Such average or summary scores are very valuable. They may be of notable service in distinguishing individuals and in predicting important facts. But they may not be measures of unitary traits; it may be misleading to call them by single names; it may be unwise to think of a person as having qualities corresponding to them." Thorndike (220:57).

3. *Personality measurement in general and the personality inventory in specific do not lend themselves to structural analysis.*

(a) "Structural analysis" . . . is . . . "segrating parts for the special study." "In biology, for example, it is impossible adequately to study the whole body at once; therefore, some part of it is isolated, either by dissection or by experimental methods that ignore more than a part. The study of anatomy is structural analysis *par excellence*. Second, a description obtained by the method of structural analysis often leads to clues about the whole from which the part was segregated." Wheeler and Perkins (253:240).

(b) "Just as the field of vision consists of a unity not to be explained by the summation of parts, so personality consists of a peculiar integration in which parts as parts are irrelevant. Here, for example, we have a peremptory challenge to the theory of piecemeal habit formation; a stalwart protest against the reduction of the individual to an agglomeration of independent bits. There is a certain pattern, a hanging-togetherness, which distinguishes the man from the sum of his characteristics." Murphy and Jensen (156:19).

3. *The personality inventory is based upon statistics which are inadequate in estimating human personality.*

"There are certain inherent limitations in the statistical method which inevitably prevent it from revealing the full unity of personality. These should be briefly considered.

"(1) Psychometrics cannot deal directly with single individuals; it has to approach them indirectly through standards established for a representative group... The *patterning* of characteristics within the single individual is entirely inaccessible to direct quantification.

"(2) Exact experimentation is forced to oversimplify, to select some specific aspect of behavior on which all subjects can be quantitatively compared..." Thus are neglected "innumerable factors, different in each individual, which determine the particular bit of behavior under examination... Here again *personal* consistency is disregarded by the exigencies of method.

"(3) When supposedly related measures fail to correspond to the degree that convention accepts as significant, the statistical method may create a false impression that the problem of consistency in personality is solved in the negative; that specificity reigns supreme. The truth may be that even low correlations may be due not to chance factors (as is usually supposed), but to the conflict of several highly consistent dispositions... Throwing together a subject whose consistency lies in an unexpected direction lowers our statistical measure, without in the slightest degree disproving the hypothesis that personality is highly consistent. If the statistical method is to be used at all, this consideration should dispose us to regard low positive coefficients as more valuable indicators than conventional practice allows.

"(4) Finally, it should be remembered that the origin, rationale, and psychological meaning of numerical results lie quite outside the scope of the statistical method." Allport and Vernon (9:47).

4. *The personality inventory presents peculiar difficulties in achieving reliability and validity.*

(a) "Investigations into the validity of measurements of personality traits always meet a great obstacle in the difficulty of securing independent measures of the traits to be studied. We may have an objective test that purports to measure one's ability to make judgments in social situations, but how are we to demonstrate that the test actually measures such ability? Where are we to secure a measure of such ability independent of our test with which to check the test results? No objective production record of social judgments on a large number of persons is available. No one form of behavior or social participation can be picked out that depends upon ability to make judgments in social situations alone. If we utilize the estimates of others as to the ability of our test to make social judgments, the estimates are subjective and are certain to be somewhat unreliable. At best the validation of our test is likely to be somewhat inconclusive." Hunt (115:324).

(b) The reliability of the personality inventory has been

attacked on the grounds of such criticisms as: "(1) Subjects do not answer reliably. (2) Answers are arranged to make a good impression; this is particularly true of the more intelligent or experienced persons, and in situations in which they suspect that their vocational status may be affected by the outcome." Watson (242:245).

(c) Spencer (192:179) believes that the reliability is likely to be higher when subjects do not sign the inventory.

(d) Also Kelly, Miles, and Terman report (125:215) that subjects are able to influence deliberately their scores on a typical personality inventory when the objective of giving the test is understood: "It is impossible to accept figures for the reliability and validity of opinion measures apart from an understanding of the way in which the test has been used. The procedure in assembling the group, in introducing, explaining, motivating, and safeguarding the opinion record, is just as important in affecting the worth of the test as anything that is printed on the paper to be handed out." (63:357).

(e) "There is at present *no perfect arbiter* of validity. Any test for personality, at least for the time being, must establish its merit through practical success as an aid in vocational guidance, and in the general analysis of cases in clinics and bureaus for personality study." Allport, G. W. (5:133).

5. *The personality inventory is based upon scoring methods that may be questioned.*

(a) "What science means by a perfectly 'objective' scale is a scale in respect to which all competent thinkers agree. A perfectly 'subjective' scale is one in respect to whose meaning all competent thinkers disagree (save by chance). These are limits between which the actual scales known to science lie." Thorndike (219:11).

(b) Spencer points out that "Current personality schedules... cannot achieve this objectivity because the items are of such nature that there can be no agreement among competent thinkers as to correct and incorrect responses. Clinical experts may find some agreement in their assumption as to how various clinical groupings may differ in their responses, but ... these assumptions have not been adequately supported by personality-test results." (192:21.)

CONCLUSIONS

Although such criticisms as listed above are frequently leveled against personality inventories, they are being widely used, especially in group studies, by psychologists of the various schools of belief. This paradox obtains largely because of lack of better instruments. Watson has something pertinent to say on this point: "I have urged that we choose units that fit the true patterns of human behavior where consistency may be expected, but I realize that this may have been the goal of many who, like myself, have failed to reach it. I have suggested that in order to create situations corresponding to these patterns we will have to guide our procedure by cues in meaningful behavior rather than by the simple constants of time and space, but please do not ask me to point to a test which gives promise in this direction. I have tried to encourage the creation of tests which help us in diagnosis as well as in symptom description, and of tests which correspond closely to the real educational objectives, but again I have had to confess that we have little which we can accept as a model." (243:71.)

Moreover, it should be remembered that the chief purpose of the proposed experiment is to determine whether stutterers as a group reveal characteristic disturbances of temperament as opposed to non-stutterers insofar as the instrument selected will allow. The purpose is not to deal directly with single stutterers but to determine whether a large, homogeneous group of stutterers presents a patterning of characteristics. Again, the purpose is not to study the total structure of personality of stutterers by means of a personality inventory but rather to see whether there is a community of sub-structures, i.e., traits of temperament or personality traits. It should be noted that no attempt is proposed to determine the interfusion of such sub-structures, if they do exist. However, if they are unearthed, insofar as the inventory will permit, they may contribute to the understanding of the *unit-multiple* manifestation of personality, stuttering.

Of the many current personality inventories, one of the most recent and widely used is the Bernreuter Personality Inventory, which was selected for the experiment. Before turning to the experiment a review of the studies pertaining to the reliability and validity of the Bernreuter Inventory seems to be in order.

III. *Validity of the Bernreuter Personality Inventory*

Does the Bernreuter Personality Inventory measure what it is designed to measure? In other words, how valid is this personality questionnaire? For with the publication of each new instrument of this type the same question has been asked. And any adequate reply must encompass certain aspects that are directly applicable to the Bernreuter Personality Inventory as well as to those upon which it is based.

Authors of the personality type questionnaire have generally followed one of two procedures in selecting valid items. The first procedure, used by Woodworth, Freyd, and Heidbreder, may be described as a careful analysis of the characteristic or trait to be measured based on the source material in the field. After the analysis is made, questions are composed to meet the demands of the revealed characteristic or trait.

The second procedure is the empirical method; that is, items are selected after a large variety of the most pertinent ones are tried out upon people who vary in the trait to be measured. Those items that are found to be most diagnostic are then selected. Ratings by associates and experts are generally used in determining the degree or variation of the subjects on the trait to be measured; or sources on already validated tests and measures are sometimes used. Bernreuter followed this second procedure. He writes: "In general, the method by which the test was constructed was to gather items to which responses could be readily made, to determine the diagnostic value of each item for each trait by comparing the responses made by groups of subjects composed of individuals who were extreme deviates in one of the traits, and to utilize these diagnostic values in making a separate scoring for each trait." (20:387.)

To determine the variations of the subject on the trait to be measured, Bernreuter used scores on already validated tests: (1) Thurstone's Neurotic Inventory, (2) Bernreuter's S-S Test of Self-Sufficiency, (3) Laird's C_2 Test of Introversion-Extroversion, and (4) Allport's A-S Test of Ascendance-Submission. The correlations between the scores made by an experimental group on the criterion tests and the scores made on the correspondence scales of the Bernreuter Personality Inventory are published by Bernreuter. The correlations corrected for attenuation—the experimental groups are small, ranging from 20 to 55 individuals—are found to approximate 1.00 in most cases.

Because the best index of the validity of any personality questionnaire is the result of continued experimentation, it seems advisable to review the studies of validity of the Bernreuter Personality Inventory since its author's initial correlational studies. Symonds (213) who carefully reviewed the evolution of the personality questionnaire, reports a growing body of evidence that attests to the validity of personality questionnaires. Others, too, have reported results which point to the validity of the Bernreuter Personality Inventory. For instance, Stagner (194), using the interview technique to arrive at a conclusion about the personality of the subject, found:

"B1-N: This scale has a high validity. Scores in the upper percentiles (above 90) apparently are invariably associated with some degree of maladjustment of importance. Scores below 90 are also important in some cases ... low scores seem quite uniformly to go with excellent adjustments. About the middle of the distribution no statement can be made.

"B2-S: This scale measures one aspect of what used to be called introversion. High scores are always associated with a certain independence (mainly intellectual) and low scores with a tendency to dislike solitude, lean on others, etc. The validity seems high throughout the distribution.

"B3-I: This scale is another measure of neurotic tendency. It does not contribute significantly to our understanding of the total personality beyond what is indicated by the other tests.

"B4-D: This scale picks out with considerable accuracy students who are likely to be ascendant, dominant or aggressive in social situations. It measures to a certain extent poise, self-possession and self-expressiveness. The high correlation with neurosis is probably excessive, being such in many cases as to mask the aggressive tendency."

Stagner concludes: "The validities of the B1-N and B2-S scales are probably as high as can be hoped for with present techniques. B4-D is somewhat inferior. B3-I might, in our opinion, be omitted from the test entirely without lowering its usefulness." (194:431.)

St. Claire and Seeger (195) studied the Bernreuter Personality Inventory scores of 1000 college students. They assumed that those students who had special conferences with the deans were more maladjusted than those students who did not have conferences. Using conferences as a criterion, they found that the former students made significantly higher scores on the Bernreuter Inventory. (They also were convinced that the B1-N and B2-S scales were independent of each other.) Such a criterion is widely acceptable by psychologists and statisticians. Lorge, for instance, has stated: "The trait can only be evaluated against psychologically significant and logically determined criteria based upon human behaviors." (139:654.)

In his *Factor Analysis in the Study of Personality*, Flanagan (72) has shown that "The scores on the four scales of the Bernreuter Personality Inventory may be largely accounted for in terms of two factors. The first is very similar to the trait measured by the tests of Neurotic Tendency and Introversion-Extroversion and has been termed 'self-confidence.' The second factor has most in common with Bernreuter's Self-Sufficiency and, reversing the sign, has been designated 'sociability,' indicating the opposite of non-sociability or independence."

* "A few of the items which were found to differentiate the individuals with high and low scores most efficiently are therefore reproduced below. The responses prefixed to the items are those of individuals having large positive scores. A few of the items most diagnostic of Factor One (i.e., confidence in oneself) are:

Yes   12   Do you blush very often?
Yes   20   Do you feel self-conscious in the presence of superiors in the academic or business world?
Yes   24   Are you troubled with shyness?
Yes   72   Are you troubled with feelings of inferiority?
Yes 103   Do you have difficulty in starting a conversation?
Yes 114   Are you troubled with the idea that people on the street are watching you?

Some of the items most diagnostic of Factor Two are:

No   13   Do athletics interest you more than intellectual affairs?

* See also pp. 88-94, 151-156.

Yes 23 Do you think you could become so absorbed in creative work that you would not notice a lack of intimate friends?

No 32 Do you prefer traveling with someone who will make all the necessary arrangements to the adventure of traveling alone?

Yes 44 Have books been more entertaining to you than companions?

Yes 61 Do you usually enjoy spending an evening alone?

Yes 109 Do you get as many ideas at the time of reading a book as you do from a discussion of it afterwards?

Yes 112 Do you prefer making hurried decisions alone?

No 121 Do you like to be with people a great deal?

A study of these and similar items suggests that Factor One may be interpreted as distinguishing between the self-confident, well-adjusted, socially-aggressive, "thick-skinned" individual and the self-conscious, shy, emotionally-unstable individual. Factor Two is perhaps best described as differentiating between the social and the non-social or independent.

Flanagan has prepared keys for scoring the Bernreuter Personality Inventory for the two traits, i.e., factors, which he arbitrarily designates as *Self-Confidence* and *Sociability*. Hence, the Bernreuter Personality Inventory can now be scored for 6 different measures of traits of personality. Most of the studies of validity of the inventory, however, were made before Flanagan's contributions were available.

IV. *The Reliability of the Bernreuter Personality Inventory*

In order to determine how accurate the adjustment questionnaire (e.g., Bernreuter Personality Inventory) is and how it compares with objective tests in better-known fields, it is necessary to review the techniques used by research workers in personality testing. Symonds (213) has put the problem neatly when he writes: "The problem of accuracy of measurement in the physical sciences comes down to the relatively simple matter of noting the variations resulting from repetitions of measurement. In psychological testing, however, it is impossible to obtain an exact repetition because, once a person has taken a test, his familiarity with it precludes setting up exactly the same conditions. The problem is solved, however, by recognizing that any test represents but a sampling of the field tested, and the repetition is accomplished by testing with another sample. The correlation between the scores on these two supposedly equivalent tests given at different sittings is used as a measure of reliability and is called the reliability coefficient."

Several techniques are employed to ascertain the reliability of adjustment questionnaire.

Repetition of the questionnaire with all the questions rewritten so as to give opposite meaning was a procedure followed by Cady (48). An example:

(First form) Do you ever have a strong desire to set fire to something?

(Second form) Do you dislike the idea of setting fire to something to see it burn?

Cady discovered that in many instances this procedure produced a new set of questions with different meanings from the original set. Hence, the two forms were not actually comparable. However, Cady (48) demonstrates that the difficulty can be largely circumvented by the use of appended explanations to the revised questions.

Retesting with the same test is sometimes used. While this procedure has been found adequate for other tests, e.g., intelligence tests, it does not lend itself effectively in the case of the personality questionnaire. Such a procedure also is time-consuming since at least a six-month period is recommended between testings.

The split-half method is a technique whereby scores on selected halves of the questionnaire, chosen at random, are correlated. The resulting correlation is then corrected by the Brown-Spearman formula, whereby one is able to estimate the correlation of the whole questionnaire against another of the same kind. For instance, Stagner (194) * used this technique in his study of the reliability of the Bernreuter Personality Inventory: "The reliabilities of the separate scales have been computed by the split-half method, using items 1-63 and 64-125. In the following table are shown uncorrected coefficients and the same after correcting for halving the data. The third column gives Bernreuter's estimated reliabilities for men.

	Original r	Corrected r	Bernreuter's Estimated r
B₁-N	.792	.88	.90
B₂-S	.672	.80	.84
B₃-I	.781	.87	.88
B₄-D	.744	.85	.88

In evaluating the split-half method, Symonds emphasizes that (1) it does not take into account differences in the subject between two sittings; (2) it is merely a measure of the internal consistency of the test items—a very important aspect of reliability, however, especially when measuring in a new field. Hence, Stagner's conclusion seems warranted "that the Bernreuter test is reliable enough for work involving group differences, but the coefficients are scarcely high enough to merit trust in individual scores if accurate measures are expected." (194:431.)

Symonds (213) presents a table of 43 reliability coefficients taken from the experimental literature. They range

* This study was made before Flanagan's additional measures were available.

from .40 on the Heidbreder Introversion-Extroversion to .95 on the Conklin Introversion-Extroversion. The reliability coefficients as a whole thus compare very favorably with similar reliabilities of recall, multiple-choice, and true-false tests. He believes that the same factors influence the reliability of questionnaires that influence the reliability of tests. There is one possible exception, however: "It has been found that questionnaires are more reliable for adults than for children because: (1) Adults are better able to introspect; (2) personal experiences, characteristics, etc., being better developed in adults than in children, stand out more clearly and are thus easier to distinguish; (3) many questionnaires—because of vocabularies used—are beyond the comprehension of children."

The reliabilities of the personality questionnaires reviewed here are generally high. The reliability coefficient of the original Woodworth Psychoneurotic Inventory is reported to be .90. That of the Thurstone Personality Schedule is said to be .946, of Laird's Colgate Personal Inventory .85, and of Chassell's Experience Variables Record .668 (average) for men and .714 for women. Coefficients of reliability representing internal consistency are high. For instance, the reliability of Allport's Test for Ascendance-Submission is said to be .78 for women repeating the test, and .74 (corrected) for men by the split-half method. Reliabilities on the Bernreuter Personality Inventory are high, ranging from .85 to .92 corrected for attenuation.

Because it has been widely used with reported high validity and reliability, and because it meets the demands of representative leaders of various points of view concerning the measurement of personality traits, the Bernreuter Personality Inventory was selected as the instrument of study reported in Chapter VIII of this monograph.

Chapter VIII

An Investigation of Stutterers by Means of the Bernreuter Personality Inventory

I. PREPARATION OF THE EXPERIMENT

Problems of Study

In planning the investigation, the problems for solution were stated as questions in the following form:

1. Do college, male stutterers have more disturbances of personality traits than college, male non-stutterers as revealed by measurements of neurotic tendency, self-sufficiency, introversion-extroversion, dominance-submission, confidence-in-oneself, and sociability?

2. Which items of the instrument, i.e., the Bernreuter Personality Inventory, as shown by an item-analysis, are there the most significant differences between stutterers and non-stutterers?

3. Are the responses of the stuttering group characteristic enough to permit a classification of personality traits or trait disturbances of stutterers?

Procedures

In order to study these questions, it was decided:

1. To obtain a group of stutterers as an experimental group and a group of non-stutterers as a control group.

2. To administer the same measuring instrument to all.

3. To compare the results obtained from the two groups.

The Bernreuter Personality Inventory * is composed of

---

* Reproduced in Appendix B by courtesy of Stanford University Press and Dr. Robert G. Bernreuter.

125 questions answered by *yes, no* and *?*; and it is scored in 6 different ways. Each scoring provides for a separate measure of a personality trait. These are: (1) a measure of neurotic tendency; (2) a measure of self-sufficiency; (3) a measure of introversion-extroversion; (4) a measure of dominance-submission; (5) a measure of self-confidence; * (6) a measure of sociability.*

4. To determine the significance of differences between the two groups, if any, in terms of the instrument used.

The question arose, how might personality tests of the questionnaire type be used to describe the personality traits of a large group of male stutterers? Primarily, it would seem, in determining whether stutterers as a group differ significantly in certain aspects of personality from non-stutterers. Since personality questionnaires have never been tried before on a large homogeneous group of male stutterers no objective evidence exists upon which to predict an answer and, therefore, such a study as the present can render a service by answering the question. If significant personality tendencies are found among male stutterers as opposed to those of non-stutterers under controlled experimentation, it seems reasonable to infer that such differences may have important implications in the corrective program for stutterers.

One other question seems pertinent concerning the use of the personality questionnaire with stutterers: May not such an instrument be designed for non-stutterers only? If the items of the inventory are studied, it will be seen that they deal with situations of everyday life. Further, it must be remembered that college stutterers are not isolated from everyday life. They must speak, go to college, work, and in general carry on like normal people despite the handicap of stuttering.

After considering the various aspects and possible appli-

* This scale was subsequently added by Dr. J. C. Flanagan.

cations of the personality questionnaire, at least three conclusions seem warranted: (1) As Lorge (138, 139) and
Wells (245) have pointed out, the personality questionnaire must be used very cautiously, if at all, as a measure
of a single individual; (2) according to Symonds (213) and
others, at the present stage of development the personality
questionnaire is best adapted to group comparisons; (3) in
light of the research of the Commission on Character Education (63) the personality questionnaire appears to be
valid for use by trained research workers only.

The instrument

With these considerations in mind, the Bernreuter Personality Inventory was selected as the instrument of measurement because:

1. The Bernreuter Personality Inventory correlates
highly with the most commonly used personality questionnaires and is as reliable as any.

2. The 125 items of the inventory seem to be representative of the ordinary experience of college students of late
adolescence whether they be stutterers or non-stutterers.

3. The inventory can be filled out in half an hour or
less, an important consideration in dealing with large
numbers of students.

4. When the study was initiated, the Bernreuter Personality, unlike most other instruments of the same type,
provided four measures of personality instead of one.
Later, as the result of Flanagan's work (72), two additional
measures of personality were provided by the same inventory. Hence, a multiplicity of measures of traits of personality seemed to increase the value and effectiveness of an
inventory in a study where time was an important factor.

The method of selecting the experimental group

The study was made possible through the co-operation
of the staff and students of the Speech Clinic of the College

of the City of New York. Each entering freshman at the College of the City of New York is required to take an oral examination in speech to determine whether he has defects of speech serious enough to warrant compulsory attendance at the clinic. The examination * is composed of two parts, oral reading and extemporized speaking. ["It is not uncommon to find students who read passably but who stutter only in extemporaneous speaking, or vice versa. Therefore, both oral reading and extemporized speaking should be tested." (16:16.)] The examination is administered by a committee of experienced speech clinicians. Because of the large numbers examined—12,866 during 6 years (spring 1931 to fall 1936 inclusive)—it is possible to select only the most serious cases of stuttering, sigmatism, lalling, hypacusia, barbarolalia, dysphonia, etc., for clinical treatment." (16:1.)

Although 416 stutterers were admitted to the City College Speech Clinic during the years 1931-1936 only 249 of them were found "serious" by unanimous vote of the examining committee of three experienced speech clinicians who had been working together and using the same criteria of selection for from 6 to 10 years. Consequently it was deemed advisable to select the "serious" group for this study. These numbered 249.

The method of selecting the control group

With the co-operation of the Personnel Bureau of the College of the City of New York 303 non-stuttering students were obtained as a control group. These 303 students were given the Bernreuter Personality Inventory under the same conditions as the 249 stuttering students.

Descriptive data pertaining to both groups

The students of both groups were all male freshmen. Because students, in order to become matriculated in the

* See Appendix A.

College of the City of New York, must (1) be citizens of
New York City, (2) be graduated from the New York City
High Schools or take qualifying examinations at entrance,
(3) have maintained an average of at least 80 per cent in
at least 15 units of courses throughout their high school
curriculum, the two groups may be said to be uniform.
For instance, the stuttering group revealed an average age
of 17 years, 2 months, the youngest stutterer being 14
years and the oldest 23 years, 7 months. The control group
averaged 17 years, with a range from 14 years, 5 months,
in the case of the youngest, to 24 years and 5 months in
the case of the oldest. All the stutterers were graduates of
New York High Schools and the same was true of all the
controls except 5. Because of the high scholastic require-
ment for entrance, both groups represented the highest
third of their respective graduating classes in high school.
Members of both groups were given the Bernreuter Personality Inventory during their first term in college.

Motivation

The Bernreuter Personality Inventory was administered
by the same examiner, i.e., the writer, who administered
the entrance questionnaire and the Psychological Examination. Groups of about 100 stutterers and non-stutterers
were given the inventory together. This method was
deemed preferable to administering the inventory to the
stutterers alone because it was assumed that there would
be less likelihood of suspicion arising in the stutterers'
minds concerning the motive behind the administration
of the inventory. Then, too, the examiner in his remarks
took the position that the administration of the inventory
was a continuation of the general testing program. He
said, before each group filled out the inventory: "It is
very good of you to come at this hour. As you may know,
we are trying to provide the most objective and therefore

the most satisfactory means of helping you to personal, vocational, and educational guidance. During freshman week you took an intelligence test and answered a long questionnaire. You are now going to take another dealing with the measurement of certain aspects of personality. The personality inventory is not long. Some of you will complete filling it out in about 15 minutes, and all of you should be finished with it within a half hour. Just as soon as a notice is posted to the effect that your inventory has been scored, you may report to the Personnel Bureau for a conference. You are not compelled to report for a conference, however. We will now distribute copies of the inventory. When you receive your copy, sign your name, read the directions, and then fill out the inventory according to the directions. If the directions are not clear, raise your hand, and one of the proctors will assist you. Thank you for your co-operation."

II. RESULTS OF THE STUDY

The first question set forth for study was: "Do stutterers have more disturbances of personality traits than non-stutterers as revealed by measurements of neurotic tendency, self-sufficiency, introversion-extroversion, dominance-submission, confidence in oneself, and sociability?

Before presenting the statistical results it may be helpful to review the description of the six measures of the Bernreuter Personality Inventory.

The Measure of Neurotic Tendency *

"High B1-N. The individual who scores high on the B1-N scale shows a tendency toward neurotic condition. Such an individual often feels miserable, is sensitive to blame, and is troubled by useless thoughts, by shyness and by feeling of

* Reproduced with permission of Stanford University Press and Professor Robert G. Bernreuter of Pennsylvania State College.

inferiority. He feels shut off from other people, he frequently day-dreams, and worries both over things that have happened and over things that may happen. He tends to score low on the B2-S scale, high on the B3-I, and low on the B4-D.

"Low B1-N. The individual who scores low on the B1-N scale is an emotionally stable person. He is rarely troubled by moods, by worries, or by criticisms of others. He is self-confident, and is a doer rather than a day-dreamer. He tends also to score high on the B2-S scale, low on the B3-I, and high on the B4-D.

The Measure of Self-Sufficiency

"High B2S. The individual who scores high on the B2-S scale is a self-sufficient person. He is able to be contented when by himself. He prefers to work alone and depends upon his own judgment in reaching decisions and in formulating plans. He tends also to score low on the B1-N scale, low on the B3-I, and high on the B4-D.

"Low B2-S. The individual who scores low on the B2-S scale is dependent upon others for his enjoyments. He likes to be with other people a great deal, and prefers company both while working and during leisure hours. He prefers to talk problems over with others and to receive advice before reaching decisions. He tends also to score high on the B1-N scale, high on the B3-I, and low on the B4-D.

The Measure of Introversion-Extroversion

"High B3-I. The individual who scores high on the B3-I scale is introverted in the sense that he is introspective and is given to autistic thinking. He shows the symptoms of a neurotic condition which are typical of those individuals who score high on the B1-N scale. He tends also to score low on the B2-S and B4-D scales.

"Low B3-I. The individual who scores low on the B3-I scale is extroverted in the sense that he rarely substitutes day-dreaming for action. He is emotionally stable and possesses the characteristics of those individuals who score low on the B1-N scale. He tends also to score high on the B2-S and B4-D scales.

The Measure of Dominance-Submission

"High B4-D. The individual who scores high on the B4-D scale is dominant in face-to-face situations with his equals. He is self-confident and aggressive, and readily assumes a position in the foreground at social functions. He converses readily with strangers or with prominent people and suffers no feeling of inferiority when doing so. He tends also to score low on the B1-N scale, low on the B3-I, and high on the B2-S.

"Low B4-D. The individual who scores low on the B4-D scale is submissive in face-to-face situations with his equals. He lacks self-confidence, keeps in the background at social functions, and rarely takes the initiative in directing people or activities. He experiences feelings of inferiority and is reluctant to meet important personages. He also tends to score high on the B1-N scale, low on the B2-S, and high on the B3-I."

The Measure of Confidence in Oneself

Persons scoring high on this scale tend to be hamperingly self-conscious and to have feelings of inferiority; those scoring above 98 percentile would probably benefit from psychiatric or medical advice. Those scoring low tend to be wholesomely self-confident and to be very well adjusted to their environment.

The Measure of Sociability

Persons scoring high on this scale tend to be non-social, solitary, or independent. Those scoring low tend to be sociable and gregarious.

Table 5 shows the scores made on the six scales by the two groups. From Table 5 columns 1 and 4 we may conclude that stutterers score significantly higher emotionally (Scale B1-N), are more introverted (Scale B3-I), less dominant (Scale B4-D), less confident in themselves (Scale F-C), and less sociable (Scale F-S). The total scores made up by the two groups do not differ significantly on the B2-S Scale, a measure of self-sufficiency, from a statistical viewpoint.

Table 5

DIFFERENCE IN THE MEAN SCORE ON THE BERNREUTER PERSONALITY INVENTORY OF 249 COLLEGE STUTTERERS AND 303 COLLEGE NON-STUTTERERS IN TERMS OF STANDARD ERROR OF THOSE DIFFERENCES

Group	Mean	S.D.	σ_m	Diff.	σ_d	$\dfrac{Diff.}{\sigma_d}$	In favor of
B₁–N Control	−57.02	85.82	4.93	36.36	7.50	4.84	Stutterers
B₁–N Stutterers	−20.66	89.38	5.664				
B₂–S Control	34.83	51.10	2.9356	9.926	4.3	2.300	Control
B₂–S Stutterers	24.9	45.96	2.9127				
B₃–I Control	−27.91	52.65	2.466	18.128	4.17	4.3438	Stutterers
B₃–I Stutterers	9.7	55.10	3.4922				
B₄–D Control	38.9	68.52	3.9364	26.60	7.2	3.66	Control
B₄–D Stutterers	12.30	96.38	6.1078				
F₁–C Control	−19.24	93.49	5.371	52.42	8.463	6.194	Stutterers
F₁–C Stutterers	33.18	103.31	6.547				
F₂–S Control	− 0.874	48.99	2.169	15.81	4.33	3.63	Stutterers
F₂–S Stutterers	14.94	50.01	3.8144				

In Table 6 the mean and standard deviation scores are presented for the stuttering group, the experimental group, and the group upon which Bernreuter and Flanagan established norms for college men.

If the test norms are compared with the norms of the control group, it will be seen that they are almost coincident in case of B₁-N and B₃-I, and approximate in B₂-S and B₄-D. Greater differences exist, however, in the case of the norms of F₁-C and F₂-S. It will be noticed that the control group of the experiment is larger than the group upon which norms for F₁-C and F₂-S were derived.

Table 6

COLLEGE MEN'S NORMS OF THE BERNREUTER PERSONALITY INVENTORY AS COMPARED WITH THOSE OF 249 COLLEGE MALE STUTTERERS AND 303 COLLEGE MALE NON-STUTTERERS

Measures		Test Norms for College Men	Results of 249 College Stutterers	Results of 303 College Male Non-stutterers
B_1N:	Mean	−57.3 (a)	− 20.66	−57.02
	S.D.	82.2	89.38	85.82
B_2S:	Mean	27.0 (b)	24.90	34.83
	S.D.	52.8	45.96	51.10
B_3I:	Mean	−25.6 (c)	9.7	−27.91
	S.D.	49.6	55.1	52.65
B_4D:	Mean	45.9 (d)	12.30	38.9
	S.D.	65.6	96.38	68.52
F_1-C:	Mean	−51.5 (e)	38.18	−19.24
	S.D.	86.6	103.31	93.41
F_2-S:	Mean	−25.9 (e)	14.94	− 0.874
	S.D.	59.4	48.99	50.01

(a) $N = 656$ (b) $N = 658$ (c) $N = 651$ (d) $N = 631$
(e) $N = 273$.

It will be recalled that the second and third questions set for this study were: Which items of the Bernreuter Personality Inventory are there the most significant differences between stutterers and non-stutterers? Are the responses of the stuttering group characteristic enough to permit the classification of personality traits of stutterers?

To study these two questions statistically it was necessary to adopt a calculating technique. After the inventories for the 249 stutterers and the 303 non-stutterers were scored twice with the help of a Veeder Counter,* the answers to each question were tabulated, and the results were used in the following formula (87:228):

$$E^2 = \sqrt{\frac{P_1 Q_1}{N_1} + \frac{P_2 Q_2}{N_2}}$$

E = the standard error of differences.

P_1 = the per cent of the control group answering the item *Yes, No,* or *?*.

$Q_1 = (1 - P_1)$ of the control group.

N_1 = the number of the control group (303).

P_2 = the per cent of stutterers answering the item *Yes, No* and *?*.

$Q_2 = (1 - P_2)$ of the stutterers.

N_2 = the number of stutterers (249).

To illustrate the procedure of calculation, the following shows Item 1 worked to completion.

	Yes	No	?	Total
Controls	110	163	30	303 (n)
Stutterers	97	126	26	249 (n)

The percentage values are as 97/249 or 36.30 per cent and 110/303 or 38.95 per cent.

	Yes	No	?
Stutterers	$P_2 = 38.95$	$P_2 = 50.60$	$P_2 = 10.44$
Control	$P_1 = 36.30$	$P_1 = 53.79$	$P_1 = 9.9$

* If there was a difference between the first and second scorings, the paper was scored again to determine the correct score.

The values of Q_1 and Q_2 for the *Yes, No* and *?* are obtained by subtracting each percentage value from one. Using the *Yes* value as an example:

$$(1-36.303 = 63.70 \ (Q_1)$$
$$(1-38.955 = 61.05 \ (Q_2)$$

Using these values as substitutes in the formula, the results are:

$$E \sqrt{\frac{(P_1)36.303 \times (Q_1)63.70}{249 \ (N)} + \frac{(P_2)38.95 \times (Q_2)61.05}{303 \ (N_2)}} = 4.145$$

$$\frac{\text{Diff.} - 38.95 \ (P_1) - 36.30 \ (P_2) = 2.65}{\sigma \text{ Diff.} \qquad\qquad 4.145} = .63$$

The formula used in finding the significance of the differences of the total score is the one devised by Pearson.

The results of all 125 items, in order of their significance, are represented in the following table. The items are given in sigma groupings. For instance, 7.0 to 7.5 indicates that in the following items the percentage difference was between 7 and 7½ times its standard error. Following each item of the inventory, in the parenthesis, *Y* or *N* is employed to identify the more significant of the two answers; *yes* or *no; S* or *C* is used to identify the group-stuttering or control—that had the greater percentage of reply on that answer.

ITEMS OF THE BERNREUTER INVENTORY ARRANGED IN THE ORDER OF SIGNIFICANCE OF THEIR PERCENTAGE DIFFERENCES BETWEEN A GROUP OF 249 MALE STUTTERERS AND 303 MALE NON-STUTTERERS

7.0—7.5

Do you prefer traveling with someone who will make all the necessary arrangements to the adventure of traveling alone? (Y by S)

6.5—7.0

Do you find it difficult to speak in public? (Y by S)

5.5—6.0

Do you get stage fright? (N by C)

If you are dining out do you prefer to have someone else order dinner for you? (N by C)

5.0—5.5

Do you consider yourself a rather nervous person? (Y by S)

4.0—4.5

Do you lack self-confidence? (N by C)

Have you been the recognized leader (president, captain, chairman) of a group within the last five years? (Y by C)

Are you often in a state of excitement? (N by C)

Do you feel self-conscious in the presence of superiors in the academic or business world? (Y by S)

3.5—4.0

Can you usually express yourself better in speech than in writing? (N by S)

Do you find it difficult to get rid of a salesman? (Y by S)

3.0—3.5

If you came late to a meeting would you rather stand than take a front seat? (N by C)

Have you frequently appeared as a lecturer or entertainer before groups of people? (N by S)

Are you troubled with the idea that people on the street are watching you? (Y by S)

Have you ever organized any clubs, teams, or other groups on your own initiative? (Y by C)

Do you often find that you cannot make up your mind until the time for action has passed? (N by C)

2.5—3.0

Do you worry too long over humiliating experiences? (N by C)

Are you usually considered to be indifferent to the opposite sex? (N by C)

Do you often feel just miserable? (Y by S)

Would you feel very self-conscious if you had to volunteer an idea to start a discussion among a group of people? (N by C)

Do you blush very often? (N by C)

Are you slow in making decisions? (N by C)

Do people ever come to you for advice? (Y by C)

Are you troubled with feelings of inferiority? (Y by S)

Do you ever complain to the waiter when you are served inferior or poorly prepared food? (Y by C)

2.0—2.5

Do you greatly dislike being told how you should do things? (N by C)

Do you feel that marriage is essential to your present or future happiness? (Y by C)

Does some particularly useless thought keep coming to your mind to bother you? (N by C)

Do you have difficulty in making up your mind for yourself? (Y by S)

Do you ever take the lead to enliven a dull party? (N by S)

Do you take the responsibility for introducing people at a party? (Y by C)

Do you usually try to take added responsibilities on yourself? (N by S)

Do you day-dream frequently? (N by C)

Do you dislike finding your way about in strange places? (Y by S)

Are you easily discouraged when the opinions of others differ from your own? (Y by S)

Are you much affected by the praise or blame of many people? (N by C)

Are you troubled with shyness? (Y by S)

Have you ever solicited funds for a cause in which you are interested? (N by S)

Do you usually work better when you are praised? (Y by S)

Are you greatly embarrassed if you have greeted a stranger whom you have mistaken for an acquaintance? (N by C)

Do you experience many pleasant or unpleasant moods? (N by C)

Are you thrifty and careful about making loans? (Y by S)

Are you careful not to say things to hurt other people's feelings? (Y by C)

1.5—2.0

Do you keep in the background at social functions? (Y by S)

Does admiration gratify you more than achievement? (N by C)

Do you ever argue a point with an older person whom you respect? (Y by C)

Are you able to play your best in a game or contest against an opponent who is greatly superior to you? (N by S)

At a reception or tea do you feel reluctant to meet the most important person present? (N by C)

Do you find that people are more stimulating to you than anything else? (Y by C)

Do you prefer making hurried decisions alone? (Y by C)

If you were hiking with a group of people, where none of you knew the way, would you probably let someone else take the full responsibility for guiding the party? (N by S)

Do you find conversation more helpful in formulating your ideas than reading? (N by S)

Do you usually work things out for yourself rather than get someone to show you? (Y by C)

Are you touchy on various subjects? (Y by C)

Do you think you could become so absorbed in creative work that you would not notice a lack of intimate friends? (Y by S)

Are you inclined to study the motives of other people carefully? (N by S)

Are you very talkative at social gatherings? (N by S)

Do you ever heckle or question a public speaker? (N by S)

Do you usually prefer to work with others? (N by S)

Do your feelings alternate between happiness and sadness without apparent reason? (N by C)

Are you systematic in caring for your personal property? (Y by C)

Do you worry over possible misfortunes? (Y by S)

Can you stick to a tiresome task for a long time without someone prodding or encouraging you? (Y by C)

Does it bother you to have people watch you at work even when you do it well? (Y by S)

Do you find that telling others of your own personal good news is the greatest part of the enjoyment of it? (N by C)

Are you easily moved to tears? (N by C)

1.0—1.5

Would you "have it out" with a person who spread untrue rumors about you? (N by S)

Do you like to be with people a great deal? (N by S)

Can you be optimistic when others about you are greatly distressed? (N by S)

Do you ever upbraid a workman who fails to have your work done on time? (N by S)

Do you tend to be radical in your political, religious, or social beliefs? (N by S)

Are you willing to take a chance alone in a situation of doubtful outcome? (Y by C)

Does your ambition need occasional stimulation through contact with successful people? (Y by S)

Do you consider the observance of social customs and manners an essential aspect of life? (Y by S)

If you are spending the evening in the company of other people do you usually let someone else decide upon the entertainment? (Y by S)

If you see an accident do you quickly take an active part in giving aid? (Y by C)

Do you prefer to associate with people who are younger than yourself? (Y by S)

Do you usually object when a person steps in front of you in a line of people? (N by C)

Do you frequently argue prices with tradesmen, or junkmen? (Y by S)

Do you frequently feel grouchy? (N by C)

Do your interests change rapidly? (N by C)

Do you usually try to avoid dictatorial or "bossy" people? (N by C)

Would you rather work for yourself than carry out the program of a superior whom you respect? (N by S)

Do you prefer to be alone in times of emotional stress? (Y by C)

Do you often experience periods of loneliness? (N by C)

Do you usually try to avoid arguments? (N by S)

Are your feelings easily hurt? (Y by S)

Do you usually prefer to do your own planning rather than with others? (Y by S)

Do you often feel lonesome when you are with other people? (N by C)

.50—1.0

Can you usually understand a problem better by studying it out than by discussing it with others? (Y by S)

When you are in low spirits do you try to find someone to cheer you up? (Y by S)

Are people sometimes successful in taking advantage of you? (Y by S)

Does your mind often wander so badly that you lose track of what you are doing? (Y by S)

Do you prefer a play to a dance? (Y by S)

Do you try to treat a domineering person the same as he treats you? (N by S)

Do you get as many ideas at the time of reading a book as you do from discussion of it afterwards? (Y by S)

Do you usually face your troubles alone without seeking help? (N by C)

Do you like to bear responsibilities alone? (N by S)

Have books been more entertaining to you than companions? (N by C)

Have you ever had spells of dizziness? (Y by S)

Does it make you uncomfortable to be "different" or un-conventional? (N by C)

Can you stand criticism without feeling hurt? (N by S)

Do you ever give money to beggars? (Y by S)

Do athletics interest you more than intellectual affairs? (N by S)

Have you ever tried to argue or bluff your way past a guard or doorman? (Y by S)

Do you see more fun or humor in things when you are in a group than when alone? (N by S)

Do you dislike any work which might take you into isolation for a few years, such as forest ranging, etc.? (Y by S)

Do you have difficulty in starting conversation with a stranger? (N by C)

Do you usually prefer to keep your feelings to yourself? (N by S)

Do you usually feel a great deal of hesitancy over borrowing an article from an acquaintance? (N by S)

Do you usually ignore the feelings of others when accomplishing some end which is important to you? (Y by S)

Do you especially like to have attention from acquaintances when you are ill? (Y by S)

Do jeers humiliate you even when you know you are right? (N by C)

Do you want someone to be with you when you receive bad news? (N by C)

Do you usually enjoy spending an evening alone? (Y by S)

Do you make new friends easily? (N by C)

.00—.50

Do you usually avoid asking advice? (Y by S)

Do you like to get many views from others before making an important decision? (N by S)

Does discipline make you discontented? (Y by C)

Are you considered to be critical of other people? (Y by S)

Have you ever crossed the street to avoid meeting some person? (Y by S)

Do you try to get your own way even if you have to fight for it? (Y by S)

Do ideas often run through your head so that you can't sleep? (Y by S)

Do you ever rewrite your letters before mailing them? (N by S)

III. SUMMARY OF PROCEDURE AND RESULTS OF THE EXPERIMENT

An experiment was devised to determine whether college stutterers differed from college non-stutterers in that aspect of personality generally known as temperament or personality traits. Since there was no adequate information concerning personality traits of a large group of college stutterers; and since the presence or the absence of characteristic personality traits among college stutterers might have an important bearing upon corrective procedures, the experiment was deemed important and worth while.

Three definite questions for investigation were posed: (a) Do college male stutterers have more disturbances of personality traits than college male non-stutterers as revealed by measurement of neurotic tendency, self-sufficiency, introversion-extroversion, dominance-submission, confidence-in-oneself and sociability? (b) Which items of the instrument, as shown by an analysis of the inventory, are there the most significant differences between college stutterers and college non-stutterers? (c) Are the responses of the stuttering group characteristic enough to permit a classification of personality traits of college stutterers?

Results of the measurement

In response to the first question that was raised, it was found that when a selected group of college stutterers was compared with a group of non-stutterers of the same age, sex, and educational status, there were differences shown by measures of personality traits. The mean scores of the two groups on the six measures of personality traits indicated that the stuttering group was significantly higher neurotically, more introverted, less dominant, less self-confident, and less sociable. The mean scores of the measure dealing with self-sufficiency did not differ significantly from a statistical viewpoint. Individual scores on the six measures of personality traits showed overlapping between the two groups.

In response to the second question raised, the results of a detailed statistical analysis of the 125 test items indicate that the stutterers differed significantly from the non-stutterers in respect to 25 items.

In response to the third question: when these 25 items are classified into descriptive categories, such as Symonds' (213:178) and Travis' (229:112) justify, 23 fall into the following three classifications.

Fears, worries, tensions

Stutterers more often consider themselves "a rather nervous person."

Stutterers are more often in a state of excitement.

Stutterers more often feel self-conscious in the presence of superiors in the academic or business world.

Stutterers are more often troubled with the idea that people on the street are watching them.

Stutterers more often worry too long over humiliating experiences.

Stutterers are more often troubled with feelings of inferiority.

Stutterers more often feel just miserable.

Stutterers more often lack self-confidence.

Stutterers blush more often.

Stutterers more often feel very self-conscious if they have to volunteer an idea to start a discussion.

Uncommunicativeness

Stutterers more often find it difficult to speak in public.

Stutterers more often get stage fright.

Stutterers more often express themselves better in writing than in speaking.

Stutterers complain less often to a waiter when they are served inferior or poorly prepared food.

Stutterers have less frequently appeared as lecturers or entertainers before groups of people.

Dependency, "followship" (as opposed to leadership), hesitancy of decision

Stutterers more often prefer traveling with someone who will make all the necessary arrangements to the adventure of traveling alone.

Stutterers are slower in making decisions.

Stutterers, when dining out, more often prefer to have someone else order the dinner for them.

Stutterers have less often been recognized as a leader of a group within the last five years.

Stutterers more often find it difficult to get rid of a salesman.
Stutterers have less often organized clubs, or other groups
of their own initiative.
Stutterers more often find that they cannot make up their
minds until the time for action has passed.
People come to stutterers less often for advice.

Another justification for suggesting rather arbitrary
classifications, such as those listed above, is the evidence
presented by Kimmell (129).

Avoidance reactions of stutterers

The purpose of Kimmell's study was to determine the
kinds of avoidances that stutterers reveal and the effect of
these avoidances on certain adjustments. Thirty-three autobiographies of college stutterers were studied by two
judges working independently on duplicate copies of the
autobiographies. Passages were selected as representative
of avoidance behavior, and they were classified according
to whether or not the avoidance behavior was judged to
have affected speech, home, vocational, heterosexual, or
personal adjustments.

Among the results that are pertinent here are "... under
the heading of *speech* the greatest number of avoidance
reactions occurred at the 'beyond the high school' age
level. Under the heading of *home* the greatest number
occurred at the elementary school level. Under *school* the
greatest number occurred at the high school age level.
Under *vocational adjustments* the 'beyond the high school'
age level had the greatest number. Under *heterosexual adjustments* the greatest number occurred at the 'beyond the
high school age level,' and under *personal adjustments* the
greatest number occurred at the 'beyond the high school'
age level. No avoidance reactions were reported for the
pre-school age level." (129:100.)

Not only do the results of this study seemingly justify the conclusion that stutterers show types of behavior which can be definitely classified as avoidance behavior, but they throw additional light on the concept of primary and secondary stuttering.* Further, the most commonly mentioned avoidance behaviors bear a striking resemblance to some of the 25 most differentiating items reported on pages 88-90. Here are a few examples:

1. "I remember I had someone to type me out a card with the name of sandwiches on it and when someone asked the kind of sandwiches we had I would hand them the card." (129:96.)

2. "But still I played alone a great deal because it was so much easier to adjust material environment to myself than human environment. . ." "I isolated myself into a quiet, congenial, warm Utopia over which I was complete master in every one of its varied imaginative phases." (129:97.)

3. "My only enjoyment was to work alone in the fields and dream of what a great success I was going to be. My success pictures always had the foundation of perfect speech." (129:97.) "I disliked working with anyone. That called for conversation and would not let me dream." (129:97.)

4. "About this time some of the boys started having dates with girls. Oh! I wanted to so bad. I realized that this was out of the question. I knew I couldn't talk to them without stuttering and I was too shy and too sensitive to stutter in the presence of any girl." (129:99.)

5. "I was terribly shy around them when not in the schoolroom. However, I do not think I would have been if I had not stuttered. When I saw other boys talking to some of the girls I liked I felt envious, and even hated myself because I could not talk to them too." (129:99.)

6. "I felt well enough before breakfast. Then the Num-

---

* See pages 55-57.

ber Two Breakfast in the Grill, prunes, griddle cakes, and coffee. But the syrup was soaked up too quickly, and the waiter did not bring me another pitcher till the remaining half of the cakes was cold and sodden and more leathery than is permissible even in the Grill. He forgot my coffee entirely, and I was too weak to remind him. Ordering meals, instead of getting easier through enforced practice, seems to grow more trying weekly. I have to point almost altogether now." (129:100.)

Discussion of results of the experiment

The significant items, classified arbitrarily as they are and reflecting—in most cases—adjustments to specific situations, are corroborated by widespread authoritative opinion. Solomon writes: "Stuttering may be regarded as a special situation type of anticipation, anxiety, or fear neurosis. . ." (190:239.) Krout found characteristic emotional conflict among stutterers that he treated. He states: "Because these conflicts persist, and the individual continues to be unable to solve them, stammering must be regarded as a major type of neurosis." (134:179.) Thorpe declares that "Stammering and stuttering are not primarily speech defects . . . they are rather an overt symptom of personality maladjustment of the neurasthenic variety. The stammerer is more or less of a neurotic and cannot logically expect to be free from hysterical symptoms until such time as his underlying psychological conflicts or tensions are alleviated. His speech affliction is an overt expression of inner emotional unbalance." (221:109.) Fletcher draws attention to characteristic obsession possessed by stutterers: "In the very nature of the case the perpetuation (of the stuttering) points to the presence of a certain degree of obsessional neurasthenia." (74:65.) Such conclusions, reached by authorities who support widely different etiologies of stuttering, are significant. To them, stutterers as a group have negative personality traits to a greater degree than non-stutterers.

In *Because I Stutter,* Johnson has furnished a trenchant and poignant introspective analysis of personality problems faced by stutterers. Allusion to it here is especially pertinent since it reveals the problems frequently faced by the college stutterer. He writes: "As a stutterer, I experienced a rather consistent bodily and mental state. The defect does not exist merely as an obvious inability to express myself adequately in speech; it involves a generally complicated bodily tenseness as well, and a mental uneasiness, a real fear, which is apparent, as a rule, in my halting, shrinking manner of expressing myself, my thoughts, my emotions. I tend to hold myself in because I am afraid I shall stutter." (119:19.)

Even though authoritative opinion generally corroborates these results and classifications of the results, certain interpretative precautions should be borne in mind. Might not the results be attributed to mere chance? As a matter of fact, Burnham and Crawford * filled out *two* personality inventories, one each for a pair of dice. When the numbers one or four turned up, the question was answered *yes,* when two or five, *no,* when three or six, *?.* They found that "it is perfectly possible to secure by chance, scores ... of a nature which, if made by human subjects, might be regarded as significant and which, in present practice, are frequently so interpreted." In reply to the issue raised by Burnham and Crawford it may be said that: (1) the stutterer might be expected to answer such a test haphazardly, thus reacting in a manner similar to that of chance-determined responses; (2) of more importance, however, is the fact that the Bernreuter Personality Inventory was not used in the experiment to

* Burnham, P. S., and Crawford, A. B., *Vocational Interests and Personality Test Scores of a Pair of Dice.* Journal of Educational Psychology, 26, 1936, 508-512.

analyze the personality traits of two individuals—a stutterer and a non-stutterer—as it was in the case of the Burnham-Crawford study of a pair of dice, but rather was it employed to determine what differences, if any, a *large group* of college, male stutterers reveal from a comparable group of college, male non-stutterers. Authoritative opinion and judgment allow the use of personality inventories in studies of groups; they do not favor the use of such inventories in the case of individuals.

Another pertinent question is, why were these 25 items found to be most significantly differentiating? A perusal of all 125 items reveals other items that one might reasonably expect to be more significantly differentiating than some of those included in the 25 most significant items. If so, an analysis of the most significant items (those with σ 3.0 or greater) in relation to the other items in the inventory may be revealing.

Discussion of the 16 most significant inventory items

Two items among the 16 most differentiating may be conceived as referring to comparable situations. They are: *Do you prefer traveling with someone who will make all the necessary arrangements to the adventure of traveling alone?* and *If you are dining out do you prefer to have someone else order dinner for you?* Both items may be said to reflect wide-spread dependence of stutterers upon others in situations involving the giving of orders. Yet at least two other items in the inventory, but not among the "most significant" group, involve similar dependence, namely, *If you are hiking with a group of people, where none of you knows the way, would you probably let someone else take the full responsibility for guiding the party?* and *If you are spending an evening in the company of other people do you usually let someone else decide upon the entertainment?* Why were these items not also revealed as "significantly differentiating"? The answer may well be found in the experience of the stutterers. Perhaps they as a group had experienced difficulties in making arrangements for a trip, in ordering dinner, and did not have the experience of getting lost with a hiking party or of attending parties where entertainment needed to be arranged; or, if they did have these experiences they were members of groups whose leaders were already recognized as such. Another explanation may be found in the limitations of statistical interpretation of the items. It should be noted that all four of these items reflect a "characteristic" response if not of the same statistical significance. In this connection the point of view of many psychologists may be expressed in the words of Allport and Vernon, who state: "The truth may be that even low correlations may be due not to chance factors, but to the conflict of several consistent dispositions..." "... this consideration should dispose us to regard low positive co-efficients as more valuable indicators than conventional practice allows." (9:47.)

It will be noticed that among the 16 most differentiating items are 4 which refer in general to speech, namely: *Do you find it difficult to speak in public? Do you get stage fright? Can you usually express yourself better in speech than in writing? Have you frequently appeared as a lecturer or an entertainer before groups of people?* While it is reasonable to anticipate that such items would be answered characteristically by stutterers, by the same reasoning similarly significant responses might be expected from such items as: *Do you find conversation more helpful in formulating your ideas than reading? Are you very talkative at social gatherings?*, etc. Again, a perusal of the items on pages 88-94 will reveal that all such items are answered "characteristically." Perhaps another important factor in explaining the seeming discrepancy is that some severe stutterers are relatively free from their symptoms in certain situations. From Chervin (51) down to such contemporary authorities as Steer and Johnson (200) the observation that stuttering is intermittent has been stressed. This fact, more than any other, has been the *bête noire* of most theorists of the etiology of stuttering.

During the winter of 1930 the writer assigned Lord Dunsany's *A Night At An Inn* to be rehearsed by seven severe stutterers, ranging in age from 14 to 16 years of age, who had recently enrolled in the Max G. Schlapp Mental Hygiene Clinic of the New York Post-Graduate Hospital. Four of the boys never stuttered when acting the roles. The other two with speaking parts stuttered less noticeably than when reciting memorized poetry selections, for example. However, all six of them returned to their stuttering symptoms in other speech situations in the clinic during the early weeks of their attendance. Dr. Smiley Blanton in a lecture before the New York League for Speech Improvement in 1932 reported the case history of a female public reader who never stuttered on the platform but revealed severe stuttering symptoms in talking with most individuals. Such cases are not infrequently reported by clinical workers, and they may well offer a reasonable explanation for stutterers' lack of uniformity of response on inventory items that involve speaking situations.

In the group of 16 most significant items are also found 4 which may be roughly grouped together, because they are frequently said to identify neurotic behavior: *Do you consider yourself a rather nervous person? Do you lack self-confidence? Are you often in a state of excitement? Are you troubled with the idea that people on the street are watching you? Do you often find that you cannot make up your mind until the time for action has passed?* Three of these are generalized; their responses, consequently, must in large part therefore be dependent upon interpretation of meaning. In answering them, the individual might well be expected to ask himself such questions as: "What does *often* mean?" "What does *self-confidence* mean?" Yet despite the fact that such inventory items are likely to conceal as well as to reveal thought to the individual taking the inventory, all such items were answered characteristically by the stutterers.

The 4 remaining items in the most differentiating group may be interpreted as reflecting inferiority attitudes: *Have you been recognized leader of a group within the last five years? Do you feel self-conscious in the presence of superiors in the academic or business world? Do you find it difficult to get rid of a salesman? If you came late to a meeting would you rather stand than take a front seat?* Even though these items may have as a common entity the revelation of inferiority attitude, they are highly specific. Undoubtedly stutterers are at times leaders. The writer recalls a 15-year-old stutterer, for example, who was widely known in his neighborhood as "king of the babies" because he associated with and was the recognized leader of a group of 10- to 12-year-olds. At the college, where the stutterers co-operated in this study, there was at the time a club for stutterers that had a president, secretary, treasurer, and a social committee: it had leaders.

However, as a group, the stutterers reported that they had not been leaders, and this is more reasonable than not. The item dealing with self-consciousness in the presence of superiors may be taken as especially significant since few people will deny that they feel self-conscious from time to time in such situations. The candidate defending his doctoral dissertation inevitably reports some self-consciousness in the examining situation. The employee asking for an increase in salary invariably reports self-consciousness before the "ogre-boss." That stutterers should reveal such consistent feelings may readily be traced to their apprehensiveness of broken speech. In reference to getting rid of a salesman, it may be said that many people who do not stutter report this difficulty. Others have found ways and means of getting rid of a salesman without even resorting to speech. Apparently, most stutterers have not. That stutterers as a group should prefer to stand rather than to take a front seat during a meeting in progress, may be interpreted in at least two ways: either they are more timid (inferiority feeling) or they have better manners.

To sum up the discussion of the 16 most differentiating items, it may be concluded that:

(a) The significance may be due to pure chance, or to the unreliability of the instrument; or (b) the significance may be due to factors that differentiate the stutterers as a group from the non-stutterers as a group. On the whole, the latter seems more tenable for the following reasons:

(1) The large majority of the responses of the stuttering group were "characteristic" even though just 25 of them were "characteristic" to a statistically significant degree. Another important consideration at this point is that the experimental group was not only the largest homogeneous group of stutterers ever reported studied but that the control group was larger in some cases than the groups upon which the tests of the inventory were standardized.

(2) The results indicating that college, male stutterers are significantly higher emotionally, are more introverted, less dominant, less confident in themselves, and less sociable than college, male non-stutterers are logical enough, especially when they are added to those of the experiments reported in Chapters IV and V. Here was demonstrated that in many specific manifestations of personality, stutterers differ significantly from non-stutterers. To be sure, not all the differences were of equal significance.

(3) From a phylogenetic point of view, post-pubertal stutterers reveal greater differences in the more fundamental aspects of personality and smaller differences in the more accessory aspects of personality. For example, greater differences between stutterers and non-stutterers were demonstrated in certain physiological and anatomical aspects of personality than in intelligence and silent reading

ability. Yet even in these accessory aspects, statistically significant differences were demonstrated. Perhaps greater differences in personality traits are not possible of demonstration simply because the measuring instruments are not at present so precise as they are in the case of certain anatomical and physiological aspects of personality.

With a background of the experimental literature we are now ready to consider a rationale of the stuttering personality. First, however, a consideration of the modern theories of stuttering is necessary.

Chapter IX

The Stuttering Personality

The multifarious theories of the cause of stuttering

From the days of the ancients many writers have dealt with the probable causation of stuttering. Aristotle believed that the phenomenon resulted from the inability of the tongue to keep pace with the imagination. Hippocrates attributed the malady to the presence of too much black bile in the system. Galen and, later, Francis Bacon both explained stuttering by the absence of adequate heat in the speech mechanism, especially the tongue.

In the nineteenth century a number of German surgeons held that stuttering was due to structural abnormalities of the tongue and actually performed operations in which wedges of the tongue blade were removed. Not until the close of the nineteenth century, however, was the subject of stuttering given careful consideration by physicians and psychologists. Since that time there has developed a considerable body of literature on the subject— much of it being devoted to theories of causation. Among the present-day theories there are about fifteen that are widely supported.

1. *Heredity*

Makuen reported that 39 per cent of 1000 stutterers had relatives who stuttered (144). Bryngelson found 74.6 per cent of 549 stutterers had relatives who stuttered, whereas only 11 per cent of 225 normal speakers reported stuttering among relatives (reported in 228:659). McGinnis lists two possible causes of stuttering, one of which is "an inherited predisposition of an emotional instability..." (151:78.) Wepman also found a greater incidence of stuttering among stutterers' relatives than non-stutterers (246).

The most recent as well as the most exhaustive study of the heredity of stuttering, based upon experimental and control groups, is reported by West, Nelson, and Berry (251). These researchers take into account that the inheritance of stuttering may be of two types: (1) biological; (2) social, i.e., transmitted by example, training, psychic environment, etc. They also recognize the difficulty and questionable reliability of tracing stuttering from generation to generation. However, their results are arresting: (1) They find in the family lines back of the stutterers, 210 stutterers; while in the family lines back of the non-stutterers they find only 37 stutterers, a ratio of about 6 to 1. (2) There were only 4 instances in the families of the control group in which grandparent and parent stuttered; while in the families of the stuttering group there were 56 cases in which both grandparent and parent stuttered. (3) About 8 per cent of the stuttering was explained by social transmission. (4) As is usual, male stutterers were found to outnumber female stutterers. Further, "... a male person, not a stutterer, is more likely to come from a stuttering free line than is a female non-stutterer. She is more likely to conceal and he to reveal the ancestral tendency to stutter." (251:27.) (5) In twinning families they found over 5 times the expected number of stutterers. (6) There were 2½ more sinistrals in the twinning families than in the general population.

These studies pertaining to heredity and stuttering are interesting in light of the findings of Travis, Malamud, and Thayer (232) reported in Chapter IV, because Davenport (60) has found that slender men tend to marry slender women to an extent exceeding chance expectation by 50 per cent, and fleshy men tend to marry fleshy women to an extent exceeding chance by 80 per cent. Hence, the children of these marriages tend to perpetuate these more or less pure types of physiques and predispositions, such as stuttering (?).

2. *Anatomy*

Travis, reviewing the work of Ehrenfest, states that certain stutterers, which he has examined, "have suffered from birth injuries resulting in definite neurological disturbances which were considered to be directly related to stuttering." (228:660.)

Gerstmann and Schilder report cases of post-encephalitis with speech symptoms undistinguishable from stuttering (91).

Makuen included such infectious diseases as whooping cough, measles, diphtheria, and smallpox as important factors in the etiology of stuttering (144). Bryngelson also found in his survey of 70 cases of stuttering that convulsions, meningitis, severe whooping cough, pneumonia, and diphtheria bore a close relationship to the onset of stuttering (228:661).

Morgan states that "ten to fifteen per cent of stuttering is caused by abnormalities of the peripheral organs." (155.)

Fogerty emphasizes "constitutional predisposition" in stutterers (75).

3. *Breathing*

Murray found that the breathing of stutterers was highly disintegrated (157). Gutzmann assigned stuttering to "the breathing function." (100.) Trumper discovered that "in stammerers (stutterers) there is a fundamental disturbance of the respiratory mechanism, probably of nervous origin, which results in an alteration in cerebral circulation. . ." (235.)

4. *Vasomotor changes*

Robbins, in his studies of blood disturbances in stutterers, concludes that stuttering is accompanied by "much more marked increase in brain volume than could be accounted for by either the mental or the physical word used in normal speech." "... it is reasonable to conclude that increase in brain volume is an important factor in the production of stammering (stuttering)." (177:19.)

5. *Endocrine disturbance*

da Costa Ferreira claims that stuttering is of endocrine origin (59).

Timme and others refer to speech syndromes comparable to stuttering in describing parathyroid deficiency (223) (93).

Starr believes in "the metabolic etiology of stuttering" (196), and similarly Stratton, it will be recalled, discovered that an "increase of stammering (stuttering) was found to accompany increase of creatine and creatinine in the urine, or to follow upon this." (210.)

6. *Hemisphere dominance*

Sachs says that some types of stuttering seem to indicate that the impulses which are equal in both hemispheres (of the cerebrum cortex) instead of fusing with each other harmoniously, follow each other at short intervals of time, thus interfere with each other and cause stuttering (184).

Blanton ascribes stuttering to a conflict between the functions of the thalamus and of the speech centers." "... the physical symptoms of stuttering are due to the blocking of the inhibitory and discriminative control of the cortex over the lower nerve cells, caused by emotions of embarrassment and fear, conscious and unconscious, allowing the primitive muscle groups each to tend to return to its primitive function." (28:75.)

Orton (160) (161) and Travis (229) believe that stuttering may occur during speech (speaking, writing, reading, etc.) when there is lack of hemisphere dominance or dominant gradient. Bryngelson (43) is of like opinion.

Closely allied to the Orton-Travis theory is the handedness theory. Ballard (12) and others believe that stuttering is caused by imposing right-handed habits upon the left-handed child. In his survey of speech defects among school children of London he found: "Of 545 normally left-handed children, 399 were dextro-sinistrals (that is, they were naturally left-handed but had been trained to write with the right hand), while 146 were pure sinistrals (that is, they had been permitted to continue to write with the left hand). The percentage of stuttering among the pure-sinistrals was only 1.1 per cent but among the dextro-sinistrals 4.3 per cent."

7. *Transitory auditory amnesia*

Bluemel states that "the stammerer's (stutterer's) difficulty is transitory auditory amnesia." (36.) "The verbal image is paramount in determining the nature of the words expressed; hence, if no clear-cut verbal image is in the mind, no word can be orally produced. It is no more possible for the speech organs to produce a word that is not clearly expressed in verbal imagery than it is possible for a gramophone to produce words that are not present on the record." (32:13.)

Robbins (178) states a theory of causation much like that by Bluemel.

8. *Visual central asthenia*

Swift is of the opinion that "Psychological analysis shows stuttering is an absent or weak visualization at the time of speech. This lack or weakness in visualization accounts for all the numerous phenomena of stuttering in severe, medium, or mild cases." He further contends that (a) "when visualization is present stuttering is absent; when visualization is absent stuttering is present"; (b) "the severity of stuttering varies with clearness of visualization"; (c) "visualization is slightly more frequent for past and future than for present memories." (212:83.)

9. *Psychoanalytical interpretations*

Blanton writes: "Stuttering is a symptom of an inability to adjust to the group. It is caused by fear, a timidity, or a negative (hate) attitude toward the group. The child wishes to talk with his conscious mind but with the unconscious mind there is an inhibition against speech. Stuttering is the result." (in 248:71.)

He continues: "Psychoanalysis has made a valuable contribution to the cause and treatment of stuttering. The first stage of the love life of a child is the oral erotic stage in which the child not only uses the mouth to get nourishment, but also to get sexual pleasure of the infantile type. The mouth region is highly charged with emotion, and sounds are partly made because of the pleasure they give through the stimulation of the vocal organs. The oral erotic stage passes normally. Sometimes, however, the child remains fixed in this stage and also his love energy is centered upon himself, and he becomes narcissistic. It is this narcissism which gives rise to timidity and self-consciousness." (248:71.)

Coriat says: "Thus, stammering (stuttering) becomes a neurosis in which the fixation of the libido at the development stage of oral eroticism persists into maturity. In his unconscious, and likewise in the conscious motor speech reactions, the stammerer (stutterer) remains fixed or anchored to this primitive biological stage because he has been unable to sublimate or to sublimate to a very limited degree, the original oral pleasure." (57:150.)

Stekel terms stuttering "an anxiety neurosis" (202), and Scripture calls it ". . . a psychoneurosis whose essential characteristic is the unconscious desire to avoid human society and whose mechanism consists in using ridiculous speech as a means of attaining the desired isolation." (187:162.)

Freud includes stuttering among "slips of the tongue" and attributes them to unworthy thoughts, unsocial actions and the necessity for concealment which constitute conflict between the conscious and subconscious (78).

Aikins in writing on *Casting Out the Stuttering Devil* says: "It (stuttering) is a simple matter of emotional habit which is at the root of all the phenomena that the Freudians describe in terms of 'unconscious ideas,' 'buried emotions,' and 'complexes.' " (2:137.)

Brown addressed a questionnaire to a considerable number of his colleagues concerning the cause of stuttering. He reports that the following physicians support the theory that stuttering is caused by neurosis or psychoneurosis: A. A. Brill, Sanger Brown II, Harvie de J. Coghill, James M. Cunningham, Smith Ely Jelliffe, George K. Pratt, William A. White (39).

10. *The inferiority theories*

Adler states: "... stuttering is an attempt to withdraw by means of passive resistance, from the superiority of others. It is based on an intensified feeling of inferiority whose persistent and tenaciously held purpose is to watch, examine, and steal marches..." "Their main idea is to gain a (decisive) influence by means of a masochistic attitude and to be able in addition to say, 'What would I not have accomplished had I not been a stutterer?' " (1:139.)

Appelt sees "symptoms of the inferiority complex" in stuttering (10).

11. *Voluntaristic theories*

Tomkins believes that "Stammering (stuttering) is a conflict between normal speech and a conscious effort misdirected through ignorance of its proper direction." (224:154.) He says in the same article: "Normal speech is automatic. No one knows how he speaks . . . but since he does talk, and since he does not know how he talks, then he does not talk consciously, but must talk automatically. Now it has been shown that the stammerer (stutterer) can say what he fears he cannot say. Also it is recognized that he makes an effort to talk. But since he does not know how he talks the effort conflicts with his normal automatic speech, and he stammers (stutters)." (224:155.)

Froeschels quotes Denhardt and Hoepfner as being "protagonists of the view that stuttering is a malady always connected in some way with volition." (82.)

Kleinfeld writes: "It has been observed . . . that the stutterer—whether consciously or not—often uses his speech defect to gain one or more of three ends. First of all, he sometimes learns that stuttering attracts attention. If the stutterer in childhood is pampered or given too much attention by an over-indulgent mother and others, he may continue to demand it in later life even at the sacrifice of fluency of speech. This explanation is especially tenable if the child, in the maturation process, does not attract a normal amount of attention through achievement. Secondly, the stutterer realizes, especially in his early school experience, that his speech difficulty is frequently accepted as an excuse for not reciting. Many times overly sympathetic teachers excuse the stutterer from making recitations. . . Thirdly, the stutterer excuses himself at times. That is, he rationalizes his failure to recite on the grounds that his speech handicap would nullify even the most excellent preparation. He develops an attitude of feeling justified in dodging speaking situations because of his disability; self-pity is not an uncommon experience to him. Whenever the stutterer assumes one of these attitudes he becomes a victim of a vicious circle from which he cannot extricate himself without a change of attitude, some analysis, and new speech habits." (17:248.)

12. *Fears, taboos, and personality maladjustments as causes*

Steel thinks that "The child who becomes conscious of speech difficulty develops fear of speech..." "This feeling of fear is entirely beyond his control. It arises almost unconsciously because it is the result of past experiences and cortical associations. This fear of speaking situations is the cause of acute and chronic stuttering." (198:23.)

Gifford writes... "the causes are psychologic and the spasmodic manifestations of the speech organs is only the external symptom of the deep-seated mental conflict." "...severe shocks and emotional conflicts in very early childhood remain as subconscious memories... and may continue to disturb the speech function..." (92:75.)

Ssikorski believes that traumatic and especially psychic "shock is the commonest cause" of stuttering. Frequently, the immediate effect of the shock is a period of mutism or loss of consciousness, stammering (stuttering) then ensues when these more profound disturbances subside. When stammering (stuttering) results from shock it is preceded by mutism or unconsciousness in 38 per cent of the cases. (193.)

Fogerty has called attention to the loss of speech followed by stuttering in the case of children who experienced air raids during the World War in London (75).

Dunlap traces stuttering to vocabulary taboos. "The idea is that the boy develops a street corner vocabulary not appropriate to the fireside. In the presence of his parents he starts to use an obscene word, reacts with fear, and interrupts the word. Fear becomes attached to the syllable, and the fear always interferes with its use." (66:44.) Bagby also reaches the conclusion that "...timidity, a mild form of fear, is the basis of the disturbance." (Stuttering.) He also says that "Fear accounts for the maintenance of stuttering." (11:70.)

Stivers lists seven main conflicts ". . . which tend to disintegrate the personality and which result in stammering." (Stuttering.) (207:131.)

Solomon finds that "Stuttering is an emotional and personality disorder," (190:43) and Raubicheck is of like opinion except that she adds a word concerning social environment. She writes: ". . . stuttering is not a disease in itself, but it is a symptom of an emotional imbalance, a personality disorder, or a maladjustment between the individual and his social environment." (173:33.)

Makuen hints at an obsession as a possible explanation. "Many persons stammer (stutter) under certain conditions largely because they think they will. All their past experiences with speech have combined to confirm them in the thought, and it soon becomes a sort of 'fixed idea.' " (142: 191.)

Healy has found a number of cases in which stuttering has led to anti-social reactions on the part of youth. He believes that stuttering may be a sign of degeneracy and defective traits (106).

Parker views the cause of stuttering as being "nervous instability with emotional symptoms." (164:35.)

Brown writes: "The cause of this maladjustment is, I believe, emotional, and stuttering is but a symptom of the lack of integration of the personality of the stutterer." He also reports that the following physicians hold that stuttering is caused by emotional or behavior disorders: "Drs. Forrest N. Anderson, Frederick W. Allen, William H. Burnham, V. E. Fisher, Lawson G. Lowery, James L. McCartney, Howard W. Potter, and Henry C. Shumacher." (39:150.)

13. *Bad habits as etiological factors*

According to McDowell (149) and Russell (16:262) stuttering is a collection of bad habits of speech brought about by conditioning and other factors.

Bucholz writes: "Except for their bad habits of speech there would be nothing that would even begin to distinguish them from the general average of their fellows." (45:60.)

After weighing the possibilities of causation between heredity factors and psychological factors Greene summarizes in the following words: "From all indications it is primarily psychologic rather than biologic. By it being psychologic, I mean factors of training the likes and dislikes, the bents, slants and attitudes, the character that we bring as individuals to our daily actions and associations." (98:166.)

Kenyon's theory of causation embraces the idea that the stutterer has faulty habits of phonation and voice production. The cure can best be effected by "conscious, active chest control, coupled with consciously directed production of each elemental sound of speech." (127:177.)

Wilson writes: "Whatever may have been the first cause of stuttering" there is present "a strong kinesthetic memory of tight lips, heaving chest, constricted throat, tongue cleaving to the roof of the mouth, in all an emotion-laden habit of overtensed, consequently uncontrolled muscles during speech." (255:170.)

14. *Factors of causation in societal conditioning*

Fletcher is a vigorous proponent of the theory that stuttering is caused by inimical social situations with cumulative conditioning. He says: "What is sometimes described as 'growing out' of stuttering is in reality the result of overcoming social sensitiveness by getting on a par with an increasing number of associates." (74:181.)

Gray is also of this belief. He looks on speech (normal communication) as "a form of adjustment to social life. It is influenced not only by habits which we form through education, but also by those processes which take place below the threshold of consciousness; whatever affects either of these factors, therefore, is bound to affect speech. The emotional conflicts which center about the fundamental cravings and the social restrictions result in an upset of the normal reactions, and a speech defect follows. The great problem is how to handle those conflicts so as to reduce the friction which prevents the proper expression, indeed, the proper development of the personality." (96:100.)

15. *Arrestation as a causative factor*

Steer writes: "... if the generally accepted symptoms of stuttering are really indicative, then their presence in the speech patterns of children of both types, stuttering and non-stuttering, would indicate that children in general do stutter. In other words, stuttering might be defined as a function of the maturation of the mechanism involved in speaking. And therefore, adults who stutter do so because of arrested development in the speech mechanism." (201:2.)

16. *Miscellaneous theories of causation*

Needless to say, there are many theories of the causation of stuttering that have not been developed thoroughly or considered seriously by speech pathologists. In the literature one reads, for instance, that the "phonic method of teaching reading produces too much mouth consciousness and may thus lead to the development of stuttering." Stuttering has also been connected with high blood pressure, fatigue, migraine, etc.

Summary

Here, then are widely divergent theories of the etiology of stuttering. Some of them were formulated before the recent research into the problem of stuttering. Thus, any adequate theory of the etiology of stuttering must provide for an explanation of the facts that have resulted from research.

Some established facts about stuttering

1. There are more male stutterers than female stutterers (254).
2. The greater the age, the greater the incidence of stuttering is among males than females (228).
3. Males persist in stuttering to a greater extent than females (251).
4. Stuttering is intermittent (51).
5. Stutterers can speak in unison with a group without stuttering (16).
6. Stutterers can sing without hesitating on words (16).
7. Stutterers can talk to themselves when alone (25).
8. Stutterers can talk in a chant or sing-song manner (35).
9. Stutterers can talk while crawling on their hands and knees (90).
10. Some stutterers can act roles in plays without stuttering.*
11. Some stutterers have no difficulty in speaking in certain social situations (51).
12. There is a marked tendency for the onset of stuttering to fall into three periods of life: at the onset of speech, between 5 and 7 years of age, and at adolescence (228).
13. Most stuttering, i.e., from 60 per cent to 85 per cent begins before 7 years of age (27).
14. There are more child stutterers than adult stutterers (201).
15. Some stutterers have no difficulty in oral reading (16).
16. Some people stutter in oral reading only (16).
17. Various methods are successful in correcting stuttering (248). Some stutterers react favorably to one kind of treatment and not to other kinds (248).

* See page 103.

Coordinating concepts of the etiology of stuttering

On the one hand there are at least 15 current theories of the etiology of stuttering, and on the other, a number of facts about stuttering which few if any of the theories can reconcile. Ostensibly, any new theory must take into account at least such well-established facts. Such a theory can be stated in the following propositions:

1. *Stuttering is conceived simply as a symptom.** Just as headache is generally accepted as symptomatic of an underlying disturbance, such as indigestion, astigmatism, sinusitis, pituitary unbalance, etc., so stuttering is viewed as a part of a syndrome.

2. *There are types of stuttering.* Just as there are many kinds of headache—headache of the forehead, temple, cranium; dull headache, sharp headache—so are there many kinds of stuttering in speech. This proposition is borne out by the common clinical descriptions of stuttering. A given stutterer is described as imitating vomitive actions while attempting to speak, another masticating movements, a third, tongue-sucking activities, a fourth, grimaces, a fifth, two or more of such uncontrollable activities. Recently, Matha (146) reported that severe stutterers attending a Paris clinic fell into two distinct classifications: those with predominantly tonic spasms of speech; those in which the speech spasms were predominantly clonic. Further, she found that the former were, as a group, timid, retiring, quiet, proud, and sensitive. The latter group was identified by different personality traits. They were on the whole careless, unstable, vain, talkative, and distractable. Here is a field of study that needs further cultivation.

3. *The various types of stuttering symptoms may reflect different etiologies.* The writer has worked with two cases of post-encephalitis whose speech was marked by exces-

---

* Cf. West's article (248) in which he stresses the point that stuttering may be a normal adaptation.

sively rapid clonic movements of the mandible. Although mandibular clonic movements are common among stutterers in the writer's experience, he has never seen the same kind in other cases. In both cases, the patients had not "stuttered" before the onset of encephalitis. Hence, in their cases, the stuttering may be said to have been a part of the syndrome of post-encephalitis. In contrast, the case of the stutterer who has mandibular clonic movements only when speaking over the telephone may be cited. In this case the clonic spasms are not reasonably attributable to post-encephalitis. It may also be true that the same cause of stuttering in two individuals is evinced in totally different kinds of clonic or tonic spasms.

4. *Because stuttering is conceived simply as a symptom, all or some of the theories of stuttering* (as described on pages 107-118) *may be true.* "... if a child has stuttering in his ancestry, slight precipitating factors may cause him to stutter; while, if he has no stuttering ancestors, it requires a considerable pressure to start stuttering in him." (251:29.) "Pressure" may thus be defined in terms of endocrine disturbance, imitation, conditioning, scarlatina, etc.

5. *Stuttering is conceived to be highly individualistic, that is, the symptom of stuttering must always be related to the stuttering person—his antecedents, education, physical condition, attitudes, etc., and above all, his present condition, i.e., personality.* In other words, since stuttering mars communication, a powerful expression of the total personality, it may be thought of as a personality handicap. If Robinson Crusoe stuttered when talking to his parrot, it was not as great a handicap as when he stuttered in giving an order to Friday. Stuttering, from this point of view, is manifested only in a social situation, i.e., when both speaker and audience are cognizant of it and the frustration it entails. Thus, the 3-year-old stuttering child, who does not recognize his broken speech as a barrier to communication, is lacking the psychology of the older stutterer

who is aware of his audience's cognizance of the stutter. The former does not feel inferior, or ashamed, or frustrated as the result of his tonic and clonic speech spasms; the latter does or has. In short, the fifth proposition of the coordinating theory transverses Bluemel's concept of primary and secondary stammering.*

6. *Even though stuttering is a symptom, the symptom may in turn cause certain kinds of maladjustments of temperament, especially if the symptom of stuttering has persisted long enough in situations that put a high premium on adequate oral communication.* The public school (elementary and secondary) in the United States is an institution that puts a high premium upon "adequate oral communication." In the early grades, the children themselves demand certain standards of speech. The child with foreign accent, or with cleft palate speech, or the child who stutters is frequently victimized by his more fortunate associates. It is the rare stutterer of college age who does not report that he was made miserable by the teasing of his youthful classmates. When the stutterer grows up, overt criticism concerning his speech defect may be rare among his classmates, but the remembrances of the earlier, unhappy experiences remain. Then, too, sympathetic teachers and classmates of the secondary school and college are likely to remind the stutterer of his speech handicap through their patronizing and "kindly" attitudes. Certainly, with the advent of adolescence, severe stutterers on the whole are not as attractive socially† to the opposite sex as are non-stutterers.

Now, it is reasonable to conceive of a case of stuttering that originated in, for instance, endocrinological disturbances in early childhood and persisted during the early school age of the child, or during the period when the earliest and basic speech habits were being formed. Later

* See pages 56-57.
† See page 98.

on, the child's endocrine constitution may have been brought into a state of balance, but the undesirable stuttering symptoms formed during this early period remained. Resulting from the habitual, severe tonic and clonic speech spasms in social situations, have developed certain characteristic traits of personality or temperament. Such a rationale seems especially pertinent to the many college stutterers that find correction of their handicap through speech re-education alone, i.e., personality adjustments result from corrected speech.

7. *At the college level, stutterers, because of their many common backgrounds and experiences, are likely to have certain characteristic traits of personality or temperament, i.e., "a stuttering personality."* While the results of the experiment reported in Chapter IX are corroborative of this proposition, it seems necessary to review the literature to determine what authorities have to say about "characteristic traits" of stutterers.

What authorities have to say about stutterers' personality traits

Many writers point out the close relationship that exists between stuttering and personality maladjustments. A review of the literature indicates that these personality maladjustments can be conveniently classified under a few large categories.

1. *Fears.* Steel writes: "Fear is a characteristic of all chronic stammerers (stutterers). Having had experience, they fear, and it is a fear which absolutely paralyzes speech. Many a man has gone without the necessities of life because he feared to ask for them. It is entirely useless to tell him that his fear is groundless, that his perspective is wrong, that he exaggerates the importance of free speech, and that he would do better if he would think less about himself and more about other things, because the one thing

uppermost in his mind, the one fixed idea, is the fact that he cannot speak as others speak, and nothing else in the world makes any difference to him"..."This feeling of fear is entirely beyond his control. It arises almost unconsciously..." (198.)

Bagby believes that "Fear accounts for the maintenance of stuttering." (11.)

Scripture says that the stutterer possesses "a diseased state of mind which arises from excessive timidity." (187.)

Stoddard calls "Fear, that evil genius of most stammerers." (Stutterers.) (208.)

2. *Mental Conflicts.* Among the conflicts that Stivers lists as being typical of stutterers are "conflict of curiosity," "conflict with oral expression," "conflict of self-importance," "conflict of smell," "conflict of sex," and "conflict of sensitivity." (207.)

Gifford also emphasizes that the greatest emotional disturbance experienced by stutterers is "deep-seated conflict." (92.)

3. *Anxiety.* Coriat is of the opinion that "The anxiety in stammerers (stutterers)...is caused by fear of the ego being overwhelmed." (57.)

"The morbid anxiety" in stuttering is thought by Travis to be "mainly an effect...the anxiety and fears of the stutterer are developed after the appearance of his defect." (226.)

McGinnis states that the "over-anxiety handicaps the child's (stutterer's) freedom of thought and performance." (151.)

4. *Guilt.* Blanton has found that "a sense of guilt" which "may show itself as shame, sin, inadequacy, or anxiety" is frequently a part of the stuttering picture (28).

Schroeder and Ackerson report that the main personality characteristics of the stutterer are shyness and sensitivity (185).

5. *Neurotic Tendencies*. Kleinfeld (17) has listed the following personality peculiarities frequently found in stutterers:

Shyness	Negativism	Moroseness
Egocentricity	Hypochondria	Taciturnity
Introversion	Submissiveness	Neurosis
Hysteria	Obsession	Restlessness
Anxiety	Nagging	Jealousy
Finickiness	Pampering	Exhibitionism
Insomnia	Moodiness	Compensation
Fear	Rebelliousness	Undemonstrativeness
Dextro-sinistrality	Masochism	Worry
Infantilism	Irritability	Unreasonableness

Stinchfield reports that "The effect of stuttering upon the personality of the individual ranges from mild inferiority feeling to deep depression and suicidal tendencies." (206.)

Aikens says that "Stutterers are the victims of emotional habits..." (2.)

Gifford finds that "in some temperaments stuttering may cause the character (personality) to develop along negative lines." (92.)

Scripture observes that stutterers "tend toward a condition of segregation which will enable the person to avoid speaking occasions." (187.)

Raubicheck believes that stutterers have "neurotic difficulties." (174.)

Rogers thinks that the stutterer "is one of those in whom the nervous (autonomic) system responds with more than average speed or force." (181.)

The Blantons observe that stuttering is "always superimposed on the neurotic constitution or temperament." (27.)

Blueler writes that the patient who becomes predisposed

to stuttering is confronted with a number of personality maladjustments: "The expectation neurosis usually develops more slowly than the traumatic neurosis, to which it shows a certain resemblance and also cannot be sharply differentiated from many hysterical syndromes." (31.)

Brown believes that one of the greatest needs of the stutterer is "personality integration which will enable him to adjust adequately through speech, to social situations." (39.)

West holds to the belief that stuttering "frequently alters the character, personality, and power of adaptation of an individual." (247.)

Robbins views as one of the greatest obstacles to the cure of stuttering the "emotional problem." (175.)

Makuen writes: "That many stammerers (stutterers) are profoundly neurotic must be admitted." He believes, however, that the neurotic tendency "is more largely resultant than causative." (143.)

Kenyon reports that "The disorder (stuttering) involves emotional disturbance superinduced by social relations and the accompanying act of talking." (127.)

Heltman looks upon the stutterer as one maladjusted to his environment. "It is admitted that no stutterer can recover fully till he learns to adjust himself to his environment as he finds it." (105.)

Greene thinks that the stutterer's difficulty in oral communication depends upon "hesitation conditioned on certain states of mind in the form of emotions, feelings, attitudes, or ideas." (98.)

Bucholz finds: "The mental and emotional apprehensiveness that is so closely enmeshed with the bad speech habits naturally builds itself into the psychoneurotic state of the stutterer." (45.)

Fletcher states: "It is unquestionably true that stutterers suffer from a sense of inferiority." (74.)

Bryngelson finds that "Many of them (stutterers) are discouraged with their failure in trying to understand their feelings of inferiority." (43.)

Bluemel believes that "The stammerer (stutterer) dodges people and situations. He will cross the street or turn a corner rather than face the necessity for conversation." "... not infrequently the stammerer (stutterer) remains silent rather than face the struggle of speech. Confusion is especially apt to occur when inhibition is severe." (34.)

A classification of authorities

Although the authorities on stuttering almost unanimously state that stutterers have significant personality maladjustments, they rarely state definitely whether the personality maladjustments are causative, resultant, or concomitant factors. Consequently, an attempt was made

Table 7

AUTHORITIES WHO MAY BE SAID TO HOLD THE OPINION THAT STUTTERING CAUSES PERSONALITY MALADJUSTMENTS

Authority	Position	Bibliography Reference
*Bluemel	Denver, Colo.	34
Bryngelson	Speech Clinician, Univ. of Minn.	43
Gifford	State Director of Speech Correction, California.	92
*Greene	Director, Nat'l Hospital of Speech Disorders.	98
Johnson	Speech Clinician, Univ. of Iowa.	121
*Kenyon	Professor, Rush Medical College, Chicago.	127
Stinchfield	Speech Clinician, Univ. of So. California.	205
*Swift	Boston, Mass.	212
Travis	Speech Clinician, Univ. of Iowa.	206
West	Speech Clinician, Univ. of Wis.	250

* Physician.

to classify the points of view in this respect. The classifications which appear in Tables 7, 8, and 9 contain the names of leading, present-day writers on stuttering. These writers are classified as described above on the basis of their respective writings referred to by the parenthetical numbers. It should be borne in mind that: (1) The classifications are the writer's, based on analysis of the writings. (2) Various authorities have presented varying points of view on stuttering from time to time. (For instance, Bluemel (32, 34, 35) has written three books on stuttering, each presenting a different theory of etiology. Dunlap (65, 66) has proposed two different theories, and the Blantons (25, 27, 28) have changed the emphasis on their point of view from time to time. (3) Whenever possible, the latest writings have been used for purposes of this classification.

Table 8

AUTHORITIES WHO MAY BE SAID TO HOLD THE OPINION THAT
PERSONALITY MALADJUSTMENTS CAUSE STUTTERING

Authority	Position	Bibliography Reference
*Blanton	Professor, Cornell Medical College.	25
Brown	Nat'l Comm. for Mental Hygiene	38
*Coriat	Psychiatrist, Boston.	57
Dunlap	Professor Psychology, Univ. of California.	66
Murray	Speech Clinician, Univ. of Colorado.	157
Raubicheck	Director of Speech Improvement, N. Y. C.	173
*Scripture	Professor Speech, Univ. of Vienna.	187
*Solomon	Professor, Northwestern Medical College.	191

* Physician.

Table 9

AUTHORITIES WHO MAY BE SAID TO HOLD THE OPINION THAT
PERSONALITY MALADJUSTMENTS ARE CONCOMITANTS OF
STUTTERING

Authority	Position	Bibliography Reference
Bucholz	Speech Clinician, Cleveland College.	45
Fletcher	Professor of Psychology, Tulane University.	74
Heltman	Speech Clinician, Syracuse University.	105
Kleinfeld	Speech Clinician, C. C. N. Y.	16
McGinnis	Speech Clinician, Washington University.	151
Parker	Director Speech Correction, Melbourne.	164
Robbins	Speech Clinician, Emerson College, Boston.	179
*Schroeder	Chicago, Illinois.	185
*Stivers	Los Angeles, California.	207
Stoddard	Director Speech Correction, Detroit.	208

* Physician.

In order to ascertain what the present opinion of authorities is concerning personality traits of college stutterers it was decided to compose a questionnaire and submit it to a large number of speech clinicians and authorities who work or have worked with stutterers in college. The questionnaire on page 133 was composed and sent to 50 college speech clinicians.

All but one of the selected speech clinicians replied. One authority asked to be excused from replying. Of the 48 that answered question number one, 16 answered *no,* 25 answered *yes,* and 7 replied by one of the following: *yes and no, ?,* or *doubtful.*

Table 10

YES REPLIES OF 25 COLLEGE SPEECH CLINICIANS TO THE QUESTION: "DO YOU BELIEVE COLLEGE STUTTERERS HAVE PERSONALITY CHARACTERISTICS THAT DISTINGUISH THEM AS A GROUP?"

Speech Clinician	Institution	Cause	Result	Concomitant
Blanton	Cornell Univ. (Med.)	*		
Bluemel	Colorado Univ.			*
Bronstein	Queens College			*
Cotton	Wash. State Teachers College			*
Egland	Univ. Minnesota			*
Eisenson	Brooklyn College			*
Greene	National Hospital (N. Y. C.)			*
Haefner	City College (N. Y. C.)			*
Healy	City College (N. Y. C.)			*
Kelly	Ft. Hays College (Kansas)			*
Koepp-Baker	Penn. State College		*	
Levbarg	Harlem Hospital (N. Y. C.)		*	
Meader	Russell Sage College		*	
Mills	Mt. Holyoke College			*
Murray	Univ. Denver			*
Nathanson	Univ. Penn.			*
Ogilvie	Fredonia Teachers College			*
Payne	Payne Institute (N. Y. C.)			*
Robbins	Emerson College	*		
Shackson	Hope College		*	
Shaw	Penn. Coll. for Women		*	
Stinchfield (Hawk)	Univ. So. Calif.			*
Voelker	Dartmouth			*
.........†	....			*
.........†	....			*
		2	5	18

† Requested to remain anonymous.

In Table 10 are the names and institutions of those who replied *yes* together with their responses to question 3.

In Table 11 are the names and institutions of those who replied *no* together with their responses to question 3.

Table 11

NO REPLIES OF 16 COLLEGE SPEECH CLINICIANS TO THE QUESTION: "DO YOU BELIEVE COLLEGE STUTTERERS HAVE PERSONALITY CHARACTERISTICS THAT DISTINGUISH THEM AS A GROUP?

Speech Clinician	Institution	Cause	Result	Concomitant
Fields	City College (N.Y.C.)			
Healey	City College (N.Y.C.)			
Heltman	Syracuse Univ.			*
Immel	Univ. So. Cal.		*	
Kennedy	Brooklyn College			*
Palmer	Univ. Wichita			
Ryan	City College (N.Y.C.)			
Schnapp	Kings Park Hosp. (N. Y.)			*
Simon	Northwestern Univ.			
Strother	Univ. Washington			
Travis	Univ. So. Cal.		*	
West	Univ. Wisconsin		*	
Wile	Mt. Sinai Hosp. (N. Y. C.)			
Yoakum	Ill. State Teach. Coll.			
Zimmerman	Columbia			
.........†	....			
		0	3	3

† Requested to remain anonymous.

In Table 12 are the names and institutions of those who replied *doubtful* together with their responses to question 3.

In Table 13 are tabulated the personality characteristics of college stutterers as reported by authorities in response to question 2.

Table 12

DOUBTFUL Replies of Six College Speech Clinicians to the Question: "Do You Believe College Stutterers Have Personality Characteristics That Distinguish Them as a Group?"

Speech Clinician	Institution	Cause	Result	Concomitant
Bryngelson	Univ. Minnesota		"Most Likely"	
Dawes	Ohio Univ.			*
Johnson	Univ. Iowa			
Kantner	Univ. Louisiana			*
Morris	Kansas City Coll.		"Probably"	
.........†	....			
			2 (?)	3

† Requested to remain anonymous.

Table 13

PERSONALITY CHARACTERISTICS OF COLLEGE STUTTERERS As Reported by Authorities in Response to Question 2

Characteristic	Number of Times Reported
Anxiety	6
Compensatory adjustments	3
Dependence	1
Eagerness for friendships	1
Egocentricity	1
Fears	6
Higher intelligence	1
Hypersensitivity	1
Infantilisms	2
Inferiority feelings	13
Introversion	8
Neuroticisms	9
Perseveration	1
Psychoneuroses	2
Self-consciousness	12
Shyness	8
Submissiveness	1
Suggestibility	1

QUESTIONNAIRE CONCERNING COLLEGE STUTTERERS

Submitted by James F. Bender,
Queens College, Flushing, N. Y.

1. Do you believe that college stutterers have personality characteristics (traits of temperament), aside from their speech handicap, that distinguish them as a group? . . . .

2. If so, what is the most common trait or traits? . . . .

3. If college stutterers in your estimation have characteristic personality traits, which of the following three statements seems to be most often true:
The personality traits are the cause of the stutter.
The personality traits are the result of the stutter.
The personality traits are concomitants of the stutter.

4. May I have your consent to use your name in connection with your replies?
Comment:

Discussion

Although 25 college speech clinicians state definitely that stutterers have characteristic personality traits, 16 state the contrary, and 6 are doubtful. However, of the 16 that replied *no*, 6 added notes to the effect that if the personality traits seemed characteristic, they could be attributed to the effect of stuttering. Of the 6 *doubtful* replies, 5 added similar observations. In other words, 36 of the replies of the total 48, or 75 per cent of the college speech clinicians canvassed, agreed to a greater or lesser degree that characteristic traits may be linked with stuttering in a causal, resultant or a concomitant way. Added to this, there is the almost universal agreement among writers on stuttering that stutterers have significant personality maladjustments. Then, too, the experimental evidence of the personality of stutterers, i.e., morphology (Chapter IV), mental capacities

(Chapter V), and temperament (Chapter VIII), indicates that stutterers have characteristic aspects of personality.

In the more stable aspects of personality, e.g., physique, blood chemistry, the evidence is strongest. In the less stable aspects, e.g., intelligence, perseveration, the evidence is significant. In the least stable aspects, e.g., temperament or personality traits, the evidence is indicative but not as strong as in the other two main manifestations of personality. To put the idea differently, when the more basic aspects of personality are measured, stutterers tend to differ from non-stutterers more significantly and characteristically than when the less basic, i.e., accessory aspects of personality, are measured.

By its very nature, temperament is more evanescent than morphology; hence, the former is more difficult to apprehend and measure than the latter. Moreover, there is the catholic assent that present-day instruments for the measurement of temperament or personality traits are lacking in precision.

However, since temperament finds its roots in the physical inheritance and environment of the individual—the former largely predetermined in stutterers and the latter made predominantly characteristic by stuttering—it is reasonable to anticipate greater demonstrable and significant differences of temperament of stutterers, especially post-pubertal, male stutterers, as the instruments for measuring it become more precise. Such differences may well be expected to be of either a quantitative or a qualitative kind, or both.

The dysphemograph as a useful description of the stuttering personality

There have been presented in this monograph the results of research pertinent to the personality structure of post-pubertal, male stutterers. Almost without exception, the studies have been of the group-control variety (differentialism). The composite results of the studies present a picture of the stuttering personality. Bearing in mind that each case of stuttering is unique but that stutterers as a group present differences of personality from non-stutterers as a group, the speech clinician may find practical use for the dysphemograph. With it, the clinician has a chart —established by the most recent research—on which to plot and compare the commonest personality manifestations of the individual stutterer. It provides a compact guide to the descriptive study of the individual stutterer. It presents a few buoys on the vast sea of personality study related to stuttering. The arrows indicate the way stutterers are most frequently found to depart from the norms established on non-stutterers.

TABLE 14

DYSPHEMOGRAPH

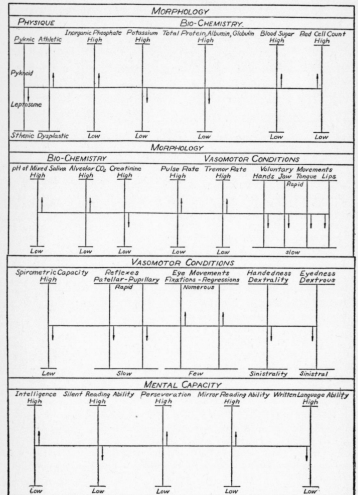

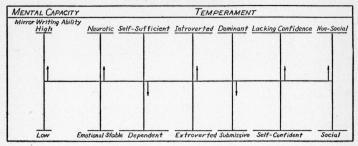

DYSPHEMOGRAPH

Chapter X

Summary, Conclusions, Implications, Discussion

A. *Summary of procedure*

1. After determining the importance of stuttering as a problem for educators, a survey of the literature of stuttering was made to determine: (a) definitions of stuttering, (b) the symptomatology of stuttering.

2. Two questions were set forth for study: (a) Do stutterers have more disturbances of personality than non-stutterers? (b) Are stutterers afflicted characteristically with certain specific peculiarities of personality?

3. In order to attempt answers to the questions set forth for study it was necessary: (a) to define personality and review the current theories of personality and its measurement; (b) to state a working hypothesis for studying the two specific questions.

4. The experimental evidence of the personality structure of stutterers was reviewed and classified under the commonly mentioned foundations of personality, i.e., morphology, mental capacity, and temperament.

5. The review of the experimental literature revealed that: (a) most of the studies pertained to post-pubertal, male stutterers, in the field of personality description known commonly as morphology and mental capacity; (b) no adequate study was discovered that dealt with temperament, i.e., personality traits, of post-pubertal, male stutterers.

6. Because the experimental evidence did not seem to include an adequate appraisal of that aspect of stutterers' personality generally known as temperament or personality

traits, it was decided to determine the possibilities of measuring personality traits of college, male stutterers.

7. An experiment was set up with the Bernreuter Personality Inventory used as the instrument of measurement.

8. Through the co-operation of the Speech Clinic of the College of the City of New York, 249 college, male stutterers were found with comparable symptoms of severity of stuttering as established by 3 experienced speech clinicians sitting as a body in conducting both oral reading and speaking examinations. Through the co-operation of the Personnel Bureau of the College of the City of New York 303 college, male non-stutterers were obtained as a control group.

9. Both groups were administered the Bernreuter Personality Inventory, their scores compared, and their responses to 125 items arranged in order of most significant differences and evaluated.

10. The results of the research and the experiment were resolved into a theory of stuttering.

B. *Summary of results*

1. Results of Chapter I:

a. Results of three original surveys were reported in Chapter I. The first dealt with the incidence of stuttering among college populations as reported by 5 institutions of higher learning that conduct entrance speech examinations by experts. It indicated that the incidence of stuttering at the college level is about 2 per cent of all entering students.

b. The second survey pertained to the incidence of articles about stuttering in the leading speech correction journal in the United States. About 50 per cent of all articles published in the *Journal of Speech Disorders* was found to be on stuttering.

c. The third survey dealt with subjects of papers presented at the early conventions of the American Speech Correction Association and published as articles in the

Yearbooks of that association. Here, approximately 62 per cent of the 108 articles were about stuttering.

The conclusions arrived at on the basis of these three surveys and other materials presented in Chapter I was that stuttering is a problem of primary importance to educators at all levels, and especially at the college level.

2. Results of Chapter II:

   a. Authorities are in agreement concerning the definitions of stuttering and stammering.

   b. Experimenters have objectively described the symptoms that comprise the stuttering syndrome.

3. Results of Chapter III:

   a. The theories of personality are conflicting.

   b. Those theories of personality that stress the whole personality pattern or the continuity of personality development are more tenable than the others.

   c. The methods and procedure of studying personality vary in reliability.

   d. A working hypothesis was stated: That stuttering entails personality maladjustments; that these personality maladjustments may be characteristic.

4. Results of Chapter IV:

   a. Research and experimentation on stuttering were explored to determine whether stutterers have more significant differences of morphology (as defined) than non-stutterers. The evidence indicated that male stutterers, especially of the post-pubertal age, showed more anomalies of morphology than male non-stutterers of the same age.

      1. Stutterers tend to have characteristic body-build.

      2. Stutterers have more disturbances of a biochemical nature.

      3. Stutterers have more vasomotor disturbances.

      4. Stutterers are afflicted with more tremors.

      5. Stutterers are inferior in control of voluntary muscular movement.

    6. Stutterers have more disturbances of the breathing function.

    7. Stutterers have more disturbances of certain reflexes.

    8. Stutterers have more vocal anomalies.

    9. Stutterers have more disturbances of eye movements.

    10. Stutterers have more disturbances of motor co-ordination.

5. Results of Chapter V:

    a. Research and experimentation on stuttering were explored to determine whether stutterers have more significant differences of mental capacity (as defined) than non-stutterers. The evidence indicated that male stutterers, especially of the post-pubertal age, showed significant differences of mental capacity when compared to male stutterers of the same age:

    1. Stutterers are afflicted with perseveration to a greater degree.

    2. Stutterers tend to be more intelligent.

    3. Stutterers are less efficient silent readers.

    4. Stutterers are more efficient in mirror-reading ability.

    5. Stutterers are less efficient in written language.

    6. Stutterers are more facile at mirror writing.

6. Results of Chapter VI:

    a. The need was demonstrated for an experiment to determine whether post-pubertal, male stutterers differ significantly from male, non-stutterers in regard to temperament, i.e., personality traits.

7. Results of Chapter VII:

    a. The personality inventory as a means of studying personality traits of temperament was explored and evaluated.

    b. The Bernreuter Personality Inventory was selected as the instrument to determine whether post-pubertal, male stutterers differ from non-stutterers in regard to traits of temperament.

8. Results of Chapter VIII:

a. The Bernreuter Personality Inventory was administered to 249 college, male stutterers and to 303 college, male non-stutterers. When the scores of both groups were compared statistically, significant differences were revealed. The stutterers as a group were found to be more neurotic, more introverted, less dominant, less confident in themselves, and less sociable. The stutterers as a group were not found to be significantly less self-sufficient from a statistical viewpoint.

b. However, individual scores in both groups overlapped on all of the scales in the Bernreuter Personality Inventory.

c. A detailed analysis of the 125 items, which comprise the inventory, revealed significant percentage differences: especially was this true of the responses of the stuttering and non-stuttering groups on 25 of the items. These items are listed on pages 88-90.

d. Although the most significant differences as revealed by 25 items cover a wide range of situations, they seem to fall into 3 fairly well-defined categories. On the basis of these categories college, male stutterers may be said: (1) to have more fears, worries, and tensions; (2) to be less communicative; (3) to be more dependent and hesitant of decision.

e. The first 16 most significantly differentiating items were evaluated in light of other similar items in the inventory.

9. Results of Chapter IX:

a. Fifteen theories of the etiology of stuttering were reviewed, and co-ordinating concepts were proposed to provide a rationale of the results reported in Chapters IV, V, and VIII.

b. The literature on stuttering was reviewed to determine what authorities have to say about stutterers' personality traits of temperament. The conclusion was drawn that authorities are almost unanimous in stating that stutterers have significant personality maladjustments.

c. The authorities were classified according to their point of view concerning personality maladjustments of stutterers.

d. The results of a questionnaire addressed to 50 college speech clinicians revealed that 75 per cent of them recognized that characteristic traits of temperament may be linked to stuttering.

e. The results of the study were presented as descriptive items of "the stuttering personality" in the form of a dysphemograph.

C. Conclusions

1. The results of this study lead to the conclusion that post-pubertal male stutterers as opposed to post-pubertal, male non-stutterers have certain characteristic differences of personality as manifested by morphology, mental capacity, and at least 5 personality traits of temperament.

2. The conclusion that college, male stutterers have characteristic traits of temperament as measured by the Bernreuter Personality Inventory seems valid because these characteristic traits have been widely noticed by experienced speech clinicians.

3. Although each case of stuttering is undoubtedly unique, the frequency of manifestation of characteristic differences of morphology, mental capacity, and temperament among groups of stutterers substantiates the theory of the stuttering personality, especially in the case of post-pubertal, male stutterers.

D. Discussion

Because post-pubertal, male stutterers as a group—as opposed to post-pubertal, male non-stutterers—reveal certain specific anatomical, physiological, and psychological anomalies of personality, and also because they differ significantly from non-stutterers upon 5 measures of personality traits, namely, neurotic tendency, self-sufficiency, introversion-extroversion, confidence in oneself, and sociability certain implications stand out:

1. The contention of those authorities on stuttering who find the handicap definitely associated with personality maladjustment seems to be corroborated.

2. However, the results would not seem to indicate for the field of personality traits a quality of uniqueness for the psychology of college, male stutterers. Their reactions would seem to follow the general pattern of the non-stutterer of college age except for a variation—in some stutterers, great variation; in others, less—from the psychology of the normal person. Support for this statment would seem to be found in the way certain stutterers have surmounted their handicap (25:119).

3. To the speech clinician the conclusions of this study, that stuttering at the post-pubertal stage is closely associated with personality maladjustments, may have important bearing upon therapeutic techniques. When stuttering is found to be co-extensive with a variety of personality maladjustments, as reported in Chapters IV, V, VIII, it is reasonable to conceive of the rehabilitation program in broader terms than only phonetic drills, breathing exercises, and relaxation techniques.

In short, the therapeutic implications of the study seem to bear out the words of Dr. Frederick W. Brown: "To those of us who would make use of the best that medical science and practice, together with psychological experimentation, observation and theorizing have to offer, the solution of the problem of stuttering appears to lie in the direction of the application of the principles of physical and mental hygiene to the treatment of the stutterer as a personality requiring integration which will enable him to adjust adequately, through speech, to social situations." (39:150.)

4. Since much is known about the personality structure of stutterers every effort should be made by educators to inaugurate and to sustain a preventive and re-educational program for incipient as well as confirmed stutterers. With such a program the incidence of stuttering among college students would undoubtedly diminish with consequential benefits to stutterers, their relatives, friends and associates, and society.

5. Since many more discoveries need to be made before the phenomenon of stuttering and its relationship to personality can be thoroughly understood, educators, especially those in charge of research and those who control the financial means of research should give careful consideration to a systematically planned research program into the field of stuttering. Groups of stutterers at the various developmental ages should be studied to determine the type of relationships that may exist between stuttering and personality factors, and also the possible shift of relationships at the various ages. Techniques representing the different philosophies of personality might be employed profitably on the same groups of stutterers. Moreover, the results of such research should be supplemented by studies of the evaluation of various corrective procedures. Only then may countless stutterers be spared from exploitation and personality maladjustment.

APPENDICES

APPENDIX A

*Directions: Read the following paragraph in a loud, clear voice
while you stand in front of the examiners' desk. When you
have read the paragraph, answer the appended question.*

Each school child of the United States of America is enjoy-
ing a rich privilege. He participates in what is unquestionably
the most complete democratic system of education that the
world has ever known. Nowhere before have there been presented to a citizenry of all ages so many choice personal advan-
tages. To the grammar school, the high school, the college, the
professional school, and the university have been added the
kindergarten, the junior high school, the vocational school,
and the junior college. Quite recently additional educational
facilities have been introduced, such as the nursery school and
adult educational forums. To be sure not every person in
America has the advantage or the natural inclination of pursuing a complete and formal education, especially one that
extends from nursery school to postgraduate study and spe-
cialization in the professional university. But the fact remains
that this country is without equal in presenting educational
facilities for a number approximately one hundred and thirty
million men, women, and children.

What are your plans for furthering your vocational
objectives?

APPENDIX B

ITEMS OF THE BERNREUTER PERSONALITY INVENTORY *

The questions on this blank are intended to indicate your interests and attitudes. It is not an intelligence test, nor are there any right or wrong answers.

In front of each question you will find: "Yes No ?"

If your answer is "Yes," draw a circle around the "Yes." If your answer is "No," draw a circle around the "No." If you are entirely unable to answer either "Yes" or "No" to the question, then draw a circle around the question mark.

1. Yes No ? Does it make you uncomfortable to be "different" or unconventional?

2. Yes No ? Do you day-dream frequently?

3. Yes No ? Do you usually work things out for yourself rather than get someone to show you?

4. Yes No ? Have you ever crossed the street to avoid meeting some person?

5. Yes No ? Can you stand criticism without feeling hurt?

6. Yes No ? Do you ever give money to beggars?

7. Yes No ? Do you prefer to associate with people who are younger than yourself?

8. Yes No ? Do you often feel just miserable?

9. Yes No ? Do you dislike finding your way about in strange places?

10. Yes No ? Are you easily discouraged when the opinions of others differ from your own?

11. Yes No ? Do you try to get your own way even if you have to fight for it?

12. Yes No ? Do you blush very often?

13. Yes No ? Do athletics interest you more than intellectual affairs?

14. Yes No ? Do you consider yourself a rather nervous person?

15. Yes No ? Do you usually object when a person steps in front of you in a line of people?

16. Yes No ? Have you ever tried to argue or bluff your way past a guard or doorman?

* Reproduced by courtesy of the author, Professor Robert G. Bernreuter of Pennsylvania State College, and of the publisher, Stanford University Press.

17.   Yes   No   ?   Are you much affected by the praise or blame of many people?

18.   Yes   No   ?   Are you touchy on various subjects?

19.   Yes   No   ?   Do you frequently argue over prices with tradesmen or junkmen?

20.   Yes   No   ?   Do you feel self-conscious in the presence of superiors in the academic or business world?

21.   Yes   No   ?   Do ideas often run through your head so that you cannot sleep?

22.   Yes   No   ?   Are you slow in making decisions?

23.   Yes   No   ?   Do you think you could become so absorbed in creative work that you would not notice a lack of intimate friends?

24.   Yes   No   ?   Are you troubled with shyness?

25.   Yes   No   ?   Are you inclined to study the motives of other people carefully?

26.   Yes   No   ?   Do you frequently feel grouchy?

27.   Yes   No   ?   Do your interests change rapidly?

28.   Yes   No   ?   Are you very talkative at social gatherings?

29.   Yes   No   ?   Do you ever heckle or question a public speaker?

30.   Yes   No   ?   Do you very much mind taking back articles you have purchased at stores?

31.   Yes   No   ?   Do you see more fun or humor in things when you are in a group than when alone?

32.   Yes   No   ?   Do you prefer traveling with someone who will make all the necessary arrangements to the adventure of traveling alone?

33.   Yes   No   ?   Would you rather work for yourself than carry out the program of a superior whom you respect?

34.   Yes   No   ?   Can you usually express yourself better in speech than in writing?

35.   Yes   No   ?   Would you dislike any work which might take you into isolation for a few years, such as forest ranging, etc.?

36.   Yes   No   ?   Have you ever solicited funds for a cause in which you were interested?

37.   Yes   No   ?   Do you usually try to avoid dictatorial or "bossy" people?

38.   Yes   No   ?   Do you find conversation more helpful in formulating your ideas than reading?

39.   Yes   No   ?   Do you worry too long over humiliating experiences?

40.   Yes   No   ?   Have you ever organized any clubs, teams, or other groups on your own initiative?

41.   Yes   No   ?   If you see an accident do you quickly take an active part in giving aid?

42.   Yes   No   ?   Do you get stage fright?

43.   Yes   No   ?   Do you like to bear responsibilities alone?

44.	Yes	No	?	Have books been more entertaining to you than companions?
45.	Yes	No	?	Have you ever had spells of dizziness?
46.	Yes	No	?	Do jeers humiliate you even when you know you are right?
47.	Yes	No	?	Do you want someone to be with you when you receive bad news?
48.	Yes	No	?	Does it bother you to have people watch you at work even when you do it well?
49.	Yes	No	?	Do you often experience periods of loneliness?
50.	Yes	No	?	Do you usually try to avoid arguments?
51.	Yes	No	?	Are your feelings easily hurt?
52.	Yes	No	?	Do you usually prefer to do your own planning alone rather than with others?
53.	Yes	No	?	Do you find that telling others of your own personal good news is the greatest part of the enjoyment of it?
54.	Yes	No	?	Do you often feel lonesome when you are with other people?
55.	Yes	No	?	Are you thrifty and careful about making loans?
56.	Yes	No	?	Are you careful not to say things to hurt other people's feelings?
57.	Yes	No	?	Are you easily moved to tears?
58.	Yes	No	?	Do you ever complain to the waiter when you are served inferior or poorly prepared food?
59.	Yes	No	?	Do you find it difficult to speak in public?
60.	Yes	No	?	Do you ever rewrite your letters before mailing them?
61.	Yes	No	?	Do you usually enjoy spending an evening alone?
62.	Yes	No	?	Do you make new friends easily?
63.	Yes	No	?	If you are dining out do you prefer to have someone else order dinner for you?
64.	Yes	No	?	Do you usually feel a great deal of hesitancy over borrowing an article from an acquaintance?
65.	Yes	No	?	Are you greatly embarrassed if you have greeted a stranger whom you have mistaken for an acquaintance?
66.	Yes	No	?	Do you find it difficult to get rid of a salesman?
67.	Yes	No	?	Do people ever come to you for advice?
68.	Yes	No	?	Do you usually ignore the feelings of others when accomplishing some end which is important to you?
69.	Yes	No	?	Do you often find that you cannot make up your mind until the time for action has passed?
70.	Yes	No	?	Do you especially like to have attention from acquaintances when you are ill?
71.	Yes	No	?	Do you experience many pleasant or unpleasant moods?

72. Yes No ? Are you troubled with feelings of inferiority?

73. Yes No ? Does some particularly useless thought keep coming into your mind to bother you?

74. Yes No ? Do you ever upbraid a workman who fails to have your work done on time?

75. Yes No ? Are you able to play your best in a game or contest against an opponent who is greatly superior to you?

76. Yes No ? Have you frequently appeared as a lecturer or entertainer before groups of people?

77. Yes No ? Are people sometimes successful in taking advantage of you?

78. Yes No ? When you are in low spirits do you try to find someone to cheer you up?

79. Yes No ? Can you usually understand a problem better by studying it out alone than by discussing it with others?

80. Yes No ? Do you lack self-confidence?

81. Yes No ? Does admiration gratify you more than achievement?

82. Yes No ? Are you willing to take a chance alone in a situation of doubtful outcome?

83. Yes No ? Does your ambition need occasional stimulation through contact with successful people?

84. Yes No ? Do you usually avoid asking advice?

85. Yes No ? Do you consider the observance of social customs and manners an essential aspect of life?

86. Yes No ? If you are spending an evening in the company of other people do you usually let someone else decide upon the entertainment?

87. Yes No ? Do you take the responsibility for introducing people at a party?

88. Yes No ? If you came late to a meeting would you rather stand than take a front seat?

89. Yes No ? Do you like to get many views from others before making an important decision?

90. Yes No ? Do you try to treat a domineering person the same as he treats you?

91. Yes No ? Does your mind often wander so badly that you lose track of what you are doing?

92. Yes No ? Do you ever argue a point with an older person whom you respect?

93. Yes No ? Do you have difficulty in making up your mind for yourself?

94. Yes No ? Do you ever take the lead to enliven a dull party?

95. Yes No ? Would you "have it out" with a person who spread untrue rumors about you?

96. Yes No ? At a reception or tea do you feel reluctant to meet the most important person present?

97. Yes No ? Do you find that people are more stimulating to you than anything else?

98. Yes No ? Do you prefer a play to a dance?

99. Yes No ? Do you tend to be radical in your political, religious, or social beliefs?

100. Yes No ? Do you prefer to be alone at times of emotional stress?

101. Yes No ? Do you usually prefer to work with others?

102. Yes No ? Do you usually work better when you are praised?

103. Yes No ? Do you have difficulty in starting a conversation with a stranger?

104. Yes No ? Do your feelings alternate between happiness and sadness without apparent reason?

105. Yes No ? Are you systematic in caring for your personal property?

106. Yes No ? Do you worry over possible misfortunes?

107. Yes No ? Do you usually prefer to keep your feelings to yourself?

108. Yes No ? Can you stick to a tiresome task for a long time without someone prodding or encouraging you?

109. Yes No ? Do you get as many ideas at the time of reading a book as you do from a discussion of it afterward?

110. Yes No ? Do you usually face your troubles alone without seeking help?

111. Yes No ? Have you been the recognized leader (president, captain, chairman) of a group within the last five years?

112. Yes No ? Do you prefer making hurried decisions alone?

113. Yes No ? If you were hiking with a group of people, where none of you knew the way, would you probably let someone else take the full responsibility for guiding the party?

114. Yes No ? Are you troubled with the idea that people on the street are watching you?

115. Yes No ? Are you often in a state of excitement?

116. Yes No ? Are you considered to be critical of other people?

117. Yes No ? Do you usually try to take added responsibilities on yourself?

118. Yes No ? Do you keep in the background at social functions?

119. Yes No ? Do you greatly dislike being told how you should do things?

120. Yes No ? Do you feel that marriage is essential to your present or future happiness?

121. Yes No ? Do you like to be with people a great deal?

122. Yes No ? Can you be optimistic when others about you are greatly depressed?

123.   Yes   No   ?   Does discipline make you discontented?
124.   Yes   No   ?   Are you usually considered to be indifferent to the opposite sex?
125.   Yes   No   ?   Would you feel very self-conscious if you had to volunteer an idea to start a discussion among a group of people?

APPENDIX C

Alveolar (a): An anatomical term, referring to a small cavity or pit as an air cell of the lungs; also pertaining to the ridge-like formations on the hard palate.

Amazonianism (n): Masculine traits of personality—physical or temperamental—in woman.

Ambivert (n): One who has both introvertive and extrovertive traits of personality.

Anthropometric Measurement (n): Pertaining to physical descriptions, indices, etc., employed by anthropologists.

Aphonia (n): Literally, "without sound." A disorder of voice—functional, psychological, or organic in cause—whose outstanding symptom is a whisper-like quality, devoid of pure tone.

Arhythmic (a): Lacking rhythm.

Asthenic or sthenic (a): A body type, marked by long, narrow, thin physique with dolychocephalic head.

Athletic (a): A body type, marked by wide shoulders, narrow waist, and well-developed, clearly defined muscular system.

Atypical (a): Abnormal; deviation from the normal type.

Auditory Amnesia (n): Lowered or lacking memory for speech sounds or words.

Barbarolalia (n): Foreign accent; outlandish dialect.

Basilic Vein (n): A vein which ascends from the base of the brain to empty into the internal cerebral.

Cephalic Vein (n): Vein which arises from the dorsal plexus of the hand.

Cholesterol (n): A monatonic alcohol found chiefly in the bile.

Clonic (klonus) (a): Pertaining to a spasm marked by regular alternation of rigidity and relaxation.

Cluttering (n): Speech marked by uncontrolled rate, repetition of words and phrases, and extraneous expressions, such as "er," "uh."

Costal Breathing (n): Breathing marked by expansion of ribs with little or no accompanying action of the diaphragmatic region.

Creatine (n): A crystallizable alkaloid found in the blood stream.

Creatinine (n): An alkaloidal derivative of creatine.

Cyclothyme (n): According to Kretschmer, a personality type marked by manic-depressive traits.

Dextral (a): Pertaining to *right*-handedness or sidedness or eyedness.

Dextro-sinistral (a): Referring to a person who is preferentially left-handed but who has learned to use the right hand dominantly.

Diaphragm (n): The membranous muscle that separates the abdomen from the thorax.

Dominant Gradient (n): A brain area which, due to its higher metabolic rate, exerts a wider influence upon the activities of adjacent areas.

Dysarthria (n): Faulty articulation caused by lesions in the nervous system.

Dysphemia (n): A syndrome of various disorders of speech caused by psychoneuroses and marked by arhythm.

Dysphemograph (n): A schematic representation of the most commonly found personality maladjustments of stutterers.

Dysphonia (n): Voice in speech marked by harshness, breathiness, stridency, etc., of organic, psychological or functional origin.

Dysplastic (a): Referring to atypical physical habitus; see page 19.

Egocentricity (n): Undue preoccupation with self.

Elektra Complex (n): A Freudian concept used to identify a complex of symptoms attributed to the suppressed sexual love of a young woman for her father.

Empirical (a): Founded on experiment, experience or observation.

Endocrine (a): Pertaining to the ductless glands or organs of internal secretion, e.g., pineal, pituitary, thyroid, parathyroid, thymus, suprarenal, gonads, etc.

Erythrocyte (n): A red blood corpuscle.

Etiology (n): Referring to causative factors; the first cause.

Eunuchoidism (n): Personality manifestations—physical and temperamental—attributed to a castrate or eunuch.

Expiration (n): The release of breath from the lungs through the mouth, or nose, or both.

Extrovert (n): One whose personality characteristics are marked by gregarious interests.

Fixation (n): A mental condition marked by preoccupation with an infantile attitude.

Functional (a): Does it function? Does it serve? A functional speech defect is an undesirable habit.

Globulin (n): A simple protein present in the blood.

Glottal (a): Pertaining to the glottis or formation of the vocal bands.

Hemisphere Dominance (n): The domination of one of the cerebral hemispheres over the other. (See *Dominant Gradient*.)

Heterosexual (a): Referring to a different sex; the opposite of homosexual.

Hypacusia (n): Lowered hearing; hearing loss.

Hyper (prefix): Excessive, above normal.

Hyperkinesis (n): Pertaining to an unusual or extreme production of motion.

Hypertonicity (n): Undue muscular tension; an excessive amount of tonus.

Hypo (prefix): Under; below normal.

Hypochondria (n): A mental disease whereby the individual is preoccupied with imaginary illnesses or morbid anxiety concerning health.

Hypokinesis (n): Pertaining to an inadequate or subnormal production of motion.

Hypomanic (a): Referring to a mild degree of mania.

Hysteria (n): A mental disease marked by uncontrollable emotionalism which usually takes the form of anesthesias, hyperesthesias, somnambulism, dream states, fugues, catalepsy, paralysis, delirium, etc.

Hysteroid (a): Resembling hysteria, characterized by perversion of inhibitory powers of the consciousness.

Infantilism (n): A childish trait, habit, or action in an older person.

Insomnia (n): Chronic inability to sleep soundly.

Inspiration (n): The intake of breath into the lungs.

Introvert (n): One whose personality traits or characteristics are marked by aloofness, taciturnity and introspection.

Kinesthetic (a): Relating to the sense of perception of movement; the muscular sense.

Kymograph (n): An instrument for recording wave-like motions; especially for recording variations in blood pressure.

Lalling (n): Faulty articulation of "l" and "r" sounds; infantile articulation.

Larynx (n): The box-like, cartilaginous structure, marked by the protuberance commonly known as Adam's Apple, which houses the organ for producing sound.

Mandible (n): Lower jaw bone.

Masochism (n): Sexual pleasure derived from feeling pain.

Mean (n): An arithmetic average.

Median (n): That point on a distribution at which 50 per cent of the scores fall on the other side.

Mirror Reading (n): A phenomenon of reading whereby the characters are read upside down.

Mirror Writing (n): A phenomenon of handwriting whereby the letters are written upside down.

Mode (n): The most frequent score of a distribution.

Morphology (n): The branch of biology dealing with form and structure.

Motility (n): Mental imagery that takes the form of inner feelings of action, such as incipient pronunciation of words, muscular innervations, and the like.

Mutism (n): Loss of speech; inability to speak.

Nagging (n): Continued carping, and disparaging criticism of a person especially concerning unimportant things or actions.

Negativism (n): A trait of personality marked by habitual unwillingness to agree to helpful and constructive suggestion. Sometimes referred to as a manifestation of subconscious hatred.

Neurasthenoid (a): Anent nervous debility resulting from prolonged mental strain, overwork, and emotional upsets.

Neurosis (n): A functional nervous disease without apparent change of nerve structure.

Nomothetic (a): Based on law; made by law givers.

Obsession (n): Preoccupation of the mind with one thought.

Oedipus Complex (n): A Freudian concept that identifies a suppressed erotic passion of a man for his own mother.

Ontogeny (n): The development of the individual as distinguished from phylogeny, or the evolutionary development of the species.

Orthodontia (n): The straightening of irregularities of the teeth.

Patellar Reflex (n): The knee jerk which customarily results when the extensor tendon is struck below the knee cap.

Peripheral (a): Pertaining to organs and structures located at or near the periphery.

Phantasy (n): An image, belief, or idea outside the pale of reality.

Phantom Speech (n): Silent, unvoiced speech during which the organs of articulation move as they do in normal speech. A corrective device for stuttering.

Phonation (n): Sustained activity of the vocal cords giving off sound.

Phonetics (n): The science of speech sounds.

Phylogeny (n): See *Ontogeny*.

Plethysmograph (n): An instrument for recording graphically the varying size of a part as determined by the state of fullness of blood it contains.

Primary Stammering (n): An inability to initiate speech because of tonic or clonic spasms.

Prodromal (a): Incipient, referring especially to the incipient stage of stuttering.

Psychasthenoid (a): Referring to a chronic mental state marked by a sense of unusualness or unreality in the afflicted person and his surroundings.

Psychoneurosis (n): A minor disease of the mind—not an insanity—marked by some idea of sensation so painful that the sufferer goes at great lengths to dismiss it from his mind.

Pyknic (a): A body type recognizable by roundness, ruddiness of complexion, brachycephalic head, etc.

Regression (n): A return to actions or attitudes that mark an earlier developmental stage; an infantilism.

Reliability (n): A quality, not a quantity, applied to a test and associated fundamentally with absence of systematic errors.

Repression (n): The thrusting back of a conscious thought into the unconscious sphere.

Rhathymia (n): A personality trait of temperament marked by carefree tendency.

Schizoid (a): Characterized by a split, broken or multiple personality; lack of personality integration.

Schizophrene (n): According to Kretschmer, a personality type marked by dissociation; a broken, split, or multiple personality.

Secondary Stammering (n): The realization on the part of the stutterer that he cannot speak. It is marked by fear which engenders a negative attitude toward speech.

Sigmatism (n): Defective articulation of the sibilant or hissing sounds in speech.

Sinistral (a): Pertaining to the left hand or side.

Somatic (a): Pertaining to the body as opposed to psychic, pertaining to the mind.

Spastic Speech (n): Marked by muscular rigidity and spasmodic movements in the production of sounds; birth-injury speech.

Standard Deviation (n): The square root of the mean of the squared deviations taken from the arithmetical mean of a distribution of scores; referred to commonly as SD or σ.

Structural Analysis (n): A method of describing personality which, because of its complexity, is analyzed by segregating parts, e.g., anatomy, traits of temperament, etc., for special study.

Sublimate (v): To direct the inimical drives and emotions into constructive, wholesome, and altruistic channels.

Supercilious (a): Referring to the muscles that activate the skin on the forehead.

Syllable (n): A vowel sound or combination of sounds containing a vowel uttered with a single vocal impulse and constituting a word or part of a word.

Symptomatology (n): That division of science that deals with symptoms of diseases.

Syndrome (n): A group or cluster of symptoms.

Thalamus (n): A division of the brain deeply imbedded in the cerebrum, and through which practically all afferent impulses must pass.

Therapy (n): A treatment or cure.

Thymus (n): An endocrine gland located near the juncture of the sternum and clavicle and especially active in early childhood when normal.

Thyroxin (n): The secretion of the thyroid gland; an active iodine compound.

Tonic (tonus) (a): Pertaining to continuous tension; the opposite of clonic.

Validity (n): A quality, not a quantity, applied to a test. When a test measures a function, simple or complex, as completely as possible, it is a valid measure of that function regardless of whether it measures with high or low accuracy.

Visceral (a): Referring to the organs lodged in the pelvic cavity.

Visual Asthenia (n): Weakened powers of visualization of words.

Voluntary Stuttering (n): The act of consciously producing the gross symptoms of stuttering.

BIBLIOGRAPHY

1. Adler, Alfred, *The Practice and Theory of Individual Psychology.* New York: Harcourt, Brace & Co., 1929.
2. Aikins, A., *Casting Out the Stuttering Devil.* Journal Abnormal and Social Psychology, 18, 1923, 137-152.
3. Allport, F. H., *Social Psychology.* Boston: Houghton Mifflin Co., 1924.
4. Allport, G. W., *Personality, A Psychological Interpretation.* New York: Henry Holt & Co., Inc., 1937.
5. Allport, G. W., *A Test of Ascendance-Submission.* Journal Abnormal and Social Psychology, 23, 1928, 118-136.
6. Allport, G. W., and Allport, F. H., *Personality Traits.* Journal Abnormal and Social Psychology, 16, 1921, 1-40.
7. Allport, G. W., and Odbert, H. S., *Trait Names.* Psychological Monographs, 47, No. 1, 1936, 1-171.
8. Allport, G. W., and Vernon, P. E., *The Field of Personality.* Psychology Bulletin, 27, 1930, 677-730.
9. Allport, G. W., and Vernon, P. E., *Studies in Expressive Movement.* New York: The Macmillan Co., 1933.
10. Appelt, A., *Stammering and Its Permanent Cure.* London: Methuen & Co., 1911.
11. Bagby, E., *Lectures on Psychology of Personality.* Whitlock's Book Store, New Haven (multigraphed), 1928.
12. Ballard, P. B., *Sinistrality and Speech.* Journal Experimental Pediatrics, 1912, 298-310.
13. Bender, I. E., *Ascendance-Submission in Relation to Certain Other Factors in Personality.* Psychology Bulletin, 30, 1933, 578.
14. Bender, J. F., *Some Questions Concerning Speech and Personality.* The Spoken Word, November 1935, 7-10.
15. Bender, J. F., et al., *Speech in College and Life.* New York: Pitman Publishing Corp., 1939.
16. Bender, J. F., and Kleinfeld, V. M., *Principles and Prac-*

tices of Speech Correction. New York: Pitman Publishing Corp., 1938.

17. Bender, J. F., and Kleinfeld, V. M., *Speech Correction Manual.* New York: Farrar and Rinehart, 1936.

18. Bernreuter, R. G., *The Imbrication of Tests of Introversion-Extroversion and Neurotic Tendency.* Journal Social Psychology, 5, 1934, 184-201.

19. Bernreuter, R. G., *The Measurement of Self-Sufficiency.* Journal Abnormal and Social Psychology, 28, 1933, 291-300.

20. Bernreuter, R. G., *The Theory and Construction of the Personality Inventory.* Journal Social Psychology, 4, 1933, 387-405.

21. Bernreuter, R. G., *The Validity of the Personality Inventory.* Personnel Journal, 11, 1933, 383-386.

22. Berry, M., *Twinning in Stuttering Families.* Human Biology, 9, 1937, 3.

23. Bills, A. G., *Stuttering and Mental Fatigue.* Psychology Bulletin, 30, 1933, 587.

24. Blackburn, W. B., *A Study of Voluntary Movements of Diaphragm, Tongue, Lips and Jaw in Stutterers and Normal Speakers,* Psychological Monographs, 41, 1931, 1-13.

25. Blanton, S., and Blanton, M. G., *For Stutterers.* New York: D. Appleton-Century Co., 1936.

26. Blanton, S., *The Medical Significance of Speech Defects.* Journal American Medical Assn., July 30, 1921, 373.

27. Blanton, S., and Blanton, M. G., *Speech Training for Children.* New York: Century Co., 1920.

28. Blanton, S., *Studies in Rhetoric and Public Speaking, in Honor of James Albert Winans.* New York: Century Co., 1925.

29. Blanton, S., *A Survey of Speech Defects.* Journal Educational Psychology, 7, 1916, 580.

30. Blom, E. C., *Mirror Writing.* Psychology Bulletin, 25, 1928, 582-594.

31. Blueler, E., *Textbook of Psychiatry.* New York: The Macmillan Co., 1924.

32. Bluemel, C. S., *Mental Aspects of Stammering*. Baltimore: Williams and Wilkins Co., 1930.

33. Bluemel, C. S., *Primary and Secondary Stammering*. Quarterly Journal of Speech, 18, 1932, 187-200.

34. Bluemel, C. S., *Stammering and Allied Disorders*. New York: The Macmillan Co., 1935.

35. Bluemel, C. S., *Stammering and Cognate Defects of Speech*. New York: G. E. Stechert & Co., 1913.

36. Bluemel, C. S., *Stammering As an Impediment to Thought*. Mind and Body, 39, 1932, 8-13.

37. Bonnet, J., *Étude Critique sur Parente Morbide du Bégaiement*. Bordeaux, 1906.

38. Brown, F. W., *Personality Integration As the Essential Factor in the Permanent Cure of Stuttering*. Mental Hygiene, 17, 1933, 266-277.

39. Brown, F. W., *The Problem of Stuttering*. In Yearbook of the American Speech Correction Assn. Madison, Wisconsin: College Typing Co., 1930.

40. Brown, F. W., *Stuttering: Its Neuro-physical Basis and Probable Causation*. American Journal Orthopsychiatry, 2, 1932, 363.

41. Browning, W., *Etiology of Stammering and Methods for Its Treatment*. Brooklyn, N. Y.: A. T. Huntington, 1915.

42. Bryngelson, B., *Phono-photographic Analysis of Vocal Disturbances in Stuttering*. Psychological Monographs, 43, 1932, 1-30.

43. Bryngelson, B., *Treatment of Stuttering*. Yearbook of American Speech Correct. Assn., 1930, 159-163.

44. Bryngelson, B., *Voluntary Stuttering*. Yearbook of American Speech Correction Assn., 1934.

45. Bucholz, C. A., *Indigenous Confidence for Stutterers*. Quarterly Journal Speech, 19, 1933, 60-64.

46. Bucholz, C. A., *Speech Correction at Cleveland College*. Yearbook of American Speech Correc. Assn., 1931.

47. Buswell, G. T., *Fundamental Reading Habits*. Supplementary Educational Monographs, University of Chicago Press, 1922.

48. Cady, V. M., *The Estimation of Juvenile Incorrigibility*. Journal Delinquency, Monographs, 2, 1923.

49. Camp, P. B., *Survey of Speech Defects.* Journal Speech Education, 11, 1923, 280-283.

50. Chassell, J. O., *The Experience Variables.* Pub. by Author, Rochester, New York, 1928.

51. Chervin, A., *Bégaiement et Autres Maladies Fonctionnelles de la Parole.* Paris: 1901.

52. Claiborne, J. H., *Stuttering Relieved by Reversal of Manual Dexterity.* N. Y. Medical Journal, 105, 1917, 577-581.

53. Cleveland, Ohio, *Annual Reports of the Board of Education,* 1927, 1928.

54. Conklin, E. S., *Definition of Introversion, Extroversion and Allied Concepts.* Journal Abnormal and Social Psychology, 17, 1923, 367-382.

55. Conradi, E., *Speech Development in the Child.* Ped. Sem., 11, 1904, 327-382.

56. Coriat, I., *Fixations of Stutterers.* Journal Abnormal Psychology, 8, 1909, 421-425.

57. Coriat, I., *Nature and Analytical Treatment of Stammering.* In Yearbook of American Speech Correct. Assn., 1930, 150-155.

58. Cross, H. M., *Motor Capacities of Stutterers.* Arch. of Speech, 1936, 112-132.

59. da Costa Ferreira, A. A., quoted in Journal American Medical Assn., 73, 1936.

60. Davenport, C. B., *Assortative Mating.* Proc. Assn. Res. Nervous and Mental Disorders, 1934, 14, 21-27.

61. Davis, Frederick, *Personal Problems Test.* Chicago: C. H. Stoelting Co., 1925.

62. Dearborne, W. F., *Nature of Special Abilities and Disabilities.* School and Sociology, 31, 1930, 362-366.

63. Department of Superintendence. Tenth Yearbook, *Character Education,* National Educ. Assn., Washington, D. C.: 1932.

64. Dunlap, K., *Habits: Their Making and Unmaking.* New York: Liveright Publishing Corp., 1932.

65. Dunlap, K., *A Possible Dietary Predisposition to Stammering.* Science, 80, 1934, 206.

66. Dunlap, K., *The Stuttering Boy*. Journal Abnormal Psychology, 12, 1917, 44-49.

67. Edgerton, H., and Patterson, D. G., *Table of Standard Errors and Probable Errors of Percentage for Varying Numbers of Cases*. Journal Applied Psychology, 10, 1926, 378-410.

68. Eisenson, J., and Pastel, E., *A Study of the Perseverating Tendency in Stuttering*. Quarterly Journal Speech, 22, 1936, 626-631.

69. Eisenson, J., *Some Characteristics of the Written Speech of Stutterers*. Ped. Sem. and Journal General Psychology, 50, 1937, 457-458.

70. Ellis, H., *A Study of British Genius*. Boston: Houghton Mifflin Co., 1926.

71. Fagan, L. B., *Relation of Dextral Training to the Onset of Stuttering*. Quarterly Journal Speech, 17, 1931, 73-76.

72. Flanagan, J. C., *Factor Analysis in the Study of Personality*. Stanford, California: Stanford University Press, 1935.

73. Fletcher, J. M., *An Experimental Study of Stuttering*. Journal Applied Psychology, 25, 1914, 201-249.

74. Fletcher, J. M., *The Problem of Stuttering*. New York: Longmans, Green & Co., 1928.

75. Fogerty, E., *Stammering*. New York: E. P. Dutton Co., 1930.

76. Fossler, H. R., *Disturbances in Breathing During Stuttering*. Psychological Monographs, 40, 1930, 1-32.

77. Francis, J. T., *A Survey of Speech Defectives of Iowa City, Iowa*. Unpublished M. A. Thesis, University of Iowa, Iowa City, Iowa, 1930.

78. Freud, S., *Psychopathology of Everyday Life*. New York: The Macmillan Co., 1914.

79. Freyd, M., *Introverts and Extroverts*. Psychology Review, 31, 1924, 74-87.

80. Freyd, M., *Personalities of the Socially and Mechanically Inclined*. Psychological Monographs, 33, No. 4, 1924.

81. Froeschels, E., *Philosophy and Asthetics of Speech*. Boston: Expression Co., 1935.

82. Froeschels, E., *Speech Therapy*. Boston: Expression Co., 1933.

83. Fruewald, E., *Intelligence Rating of Severe College Stutterers Compared to That of Other Students Entering the University*. Journal Speech Disorders, July 1936, 47-52.

84. Galton, F., *The Measurement of Character*. Fortnightly Review, 42, 1884.

85. Galton, F., *Studies of Types of Character*. Nature, 16, 1887.

86. Gardner, Warren, *A Study of the Pupillary Light Reflex with Special Reference to Stuttering*. Psychol. Monographs, 1936.

87. Garrett, H. E., *Statistics in Psychology and Education*. New York: Longmans, Green & Co., 1926.

88. Gates, A. I., *The Improvement of Reading*. New York: The Macmillan Co.

89. Gates, A. I., and Bennett, C. C., *Reversal Tendencies in Reading*. Teachers College Publication, Columbia University, 1933.

90. Geniesse, H., *Stuttering: Improvement Noted When Stutterer Spoke While Walking on All Fours*. Science, N. S., 82, 1935, 518.

91. Gerstmann, J., and Schilder, P., *Studien uber Bewegungsstorungen uber die Typenextrapyramidaler Pseudo-bulbar paralyse*. Zsch. f. d. ges. Neur. u. Psychiat., 79, 1921, 35-54.

92. Gifford, M. F., *A Consideration of Some of the Psychological Causes and Treatment of Stammering*. Yearbook American Speech Correction Assn., Madison, Wis.: College Typing Co., 1930.

93. Glaser, E. M., *Possible Relationship between Stuttering and Endocrine Malfunctioning*. Journal Speech Disorders, 1, 1936, 81-89.

94. Gordon, M. B., *Stammering Produced by Thyroid Medication*. American Journal Medical Science, 175, 1928, 360.

95. Gray, C. T., *Types of Reading Ability As Exhibited through Tests and Laboratory Experiments*. Elem. Educ. Monographs, University of Chicago, No. 1, 1917.

96. Gray, G. W., *Behavioristic Aspects of Speech Defects.* Journal Speech Education, 10, 1924.

97. Gray, W. S., *Summary of Investigations Relating to Reading.* University Chicago Monographs, 28, 1925.

98. Greene, J. S., *Stuttering... What About It?* Yearbook of American Speech Correction Assn., Madison, Wis.: College Typing Co., 1930.

99. Guthrie, E. E., *Measuring Introversion and Extroversion.* Journal Abnormal and Social Psychology, 22, 1927, 82-88.

100. Gutzmann, H., *Sprachheikunde.* Fischer's Medicin Buchhandlung, Berlin: H. Kornfeld, 1912.

101. Gutzmann, H., *Ueber das Stottern.* Berlin, 1912.

102. *Handicapped Child, The,* White House Conference Report. New York: D. Appleton-Century Co., 1930.

103. Halle, F., *Ueber Storunger der Athmung bie Stottern.* Monatach. f. Sprachheilkunde, 10, 1900.

104. Hartshorne, H., and May, M., *Studies in Deceit.* New York: The Macmillan Co., 1928.

105. Heltman, H. J., *Psycho-Social Phenomena of Stuttering, etc.* Journal Social Psychology, 9, 1938, 79-96.

106. Healy, W., *The Individual Delinquent.* Boston: Little, Brown & Co., 1922.

107. Heidbreder, E., *Measuring Introversion and Extroversion.* Journal Abnormal and Social Psychology, 21, 1926, 120-134.

108. Henrickson, E. H., *Simultaneously Recording Breathing and Vocal Disturbances of Stutterers.* Arch. Speech, 1, 1936, 133-146.

109. Herren, R. Y., *Effect of Stuttering on Voluntary Movement.* Journal Experimental Psychology, 14, 1931, 289-297.

110. Herren, R. Y., *Effects of Stuttering and Alcohol to Certain Tremor Rates.* Journal Experimental Psychology, 14, 1931, 289-298.

111. Hollingworth, H. L., *Abnormal Psychology.* New York: Ronald Press, 1920.

112. Hotelling, H., *Analysis of a Complex of Statistical Variables into Principal Components.* Journal Educational Psychology, 24, 1933, 498-530.

113. House, S. D., *A Mental Hygiene Inventory*. Arch. Psychology, No. 88, 1927.

114. Hunsley, Y. L., *Disintegration in the Speech Musculature of Stutterers During the Production of a Non-Vocal Temporal Pattern*. Psych. Monographs, 49, 1937, 32-49.

115. Hunt, Thelma, *Measurement in Psychology*. New York: Prentice-Hall, Inc., 1936.

116. Jasper, H. H., *A Laboratory Study of Diagnostic Indices of Bilateral Neuro-Muscular Organization in Stutterers and Normal Speakers*. Psychol. Monographs, 43, 1932, 72-174.

117. Jasper, H. H., and Murray, E. A., *A Study of Eye Movements of Stutterers During Oral Reading*. Journal Experimental Psychology, 15, 1932, 528-538.

118. Jennings, H. S., *The Biological Basis of Human Nature*. New York: W. W. Norton & Co., 1930.

119. Johnson, W., *Because I Stutter*. New York: D. Appleton-Century Co., 1930.

120. Johnson, W., *Influence of Stuttering on the Attitudes and Adaptations of the Stutterer*. Journal Social Psychology, 5, 1934, 415-420.

121. Johnson, W., *The Influence of Stuttering on the Personality*. University of Iowa Studies in Child Welfare. Iowa City, Iowa: University of Iowa Press, 1932.

122. Jung, C. G., *Psychological Types*. New York: Harcourt, Brace & Co., 1923.

123. Kelley, G. A., *Common Factors in Reading and Speech Disabilities*. Psych. Monographs, 15, 1932, 175-201.

124. Kelley, T. L., *Statistical Method*. New York: The Macmillan Co., 1923.

125. Kelly, E. L., Miles, C. C., and Terman, L. M., *Ability to Influence One's Score on a Typical Paper-and-Pencil Test of Personality*. Character and Personality, 1936, 4, 206-215.

126. Kennedy, L., *Speech of the Feebleminded*. Yearbook of American Speech Correction Assn., Madison, Wis.: College Typing Co., 1930.

127. Kenyon, E., *Conscious Detailed Psycho-Muscular Control of Speech Production As an Effective Basis for All*

Manner of Psychologic Treatment of Stammering. Yearbook of American Speech Correction Assn., Madison, Wis.: College Typing Co., 1930.

128. Kenyon, E., *Treatment of Stammering.* Quarterly Journal of Speech, 17, 1931, 226-235.

129. Kimmell, M., *The Nature and Effect of Stutterers' Avoidance Reaction.* Journal Speech Disorders, 1938, 3, 95-100.

130. Köhler, W., *Gestalt Psychology.* New York: Liveright Publishing Corp., 1929.

131. Kopp, G., *A Report on Bio-Chemical Studies of the Cause of Stuttering.* Speech Monographs, 1934.

132. Krausz, E. O., *Stuttering, a Disease or a Personality Problem?* Yearbook American Speech Correction Assn., Madison, Wis.: College Typing Co., 1936, 155-167.

133. Kretschmer, E., *Physique and Character.* New York: Harcourt, Brace & Co., 1925.

134. Krout, M. H., *Emotional Factors in the Etiology of Stammering.* Yearbook American Speech Correction Assn., Madison, Wis.: College Typing Co., 1936, 178-180.

135. Laird, D., *Detecting Abnormal Behavior.* Journal Abnormal and Social Psychology, 20, 1925, 128-141.

136. Liljegren, A., *Methods in the Treatment of the Stuttering Child.* Yearbook of American Speech Correction Assn., Madison, Wis.: College Typing Co., 1930, 51.

137. Lorge, I., *Personality Traits by Fiat, I, The Analysis of the Total Traits Scores and Keys of the Bernreuter Personality Inventory.* Journal Educational Psychology, 26, 1935, 273.

138. Lorge, I., *Personality Traits by Fiat, II.* Journal Educational Psychology, 26, 1935, 427.

139. Lorge, I., *Personality Traits by Fiat: A Correction.* Journal Educational Psychology, 26, 1935, 653-4.

140. Louttit, C. M., and Halls, E. C., *Survey of Speech Defects among Public School Children of Indiana.* Journal Speech Disorders, 1936, 73-80.

141. Macurdy, J. T., *Common Principles in Psychology and Physiology.* New York: The Macmillan Co., 1928.

142. Makuen, G. H., *A Brief History of the Treatment of*

Stammering. Philadelphia Medical Journal, 13, 1909-10, 191-197.

143. Makuen, G. H., *Diagnosis and Treatment of Some Functional Forms of Defective Speech.* Philadelphia Medical Journal, 7, 1901, 25-28.

144. Makuen, G. H., *A Study of 1000 Cases of Stammering with Special Reference to the Etiology and Treatment of the Affection.* Therapeutic Gazette, 38, 1914, 385-390.

145. Marston, L. R., *The Emotions of Young Children.* University of Iowa Studies in Child Welfare. Iowa City: Iowa University Press, 1925.

146. Matha, L., *Démonstration de Technique Rééducation des Troubles Psycho-neuro-moteurs du type Bégaiement Tonique.* Revue Française de Phoniatrie, 22, 1938, 99-126.

147. Matthews, E. A., *A Study of Emotional Stability of Children.* Journal of Delinquency, 8, 1923, 1-40.

148. May, M. A., Hartshorne, H., Welty, R. E., *Personality and Character Tests.* Psychology Bulletin, 1927, 418-435; 25, 1928, 422-439; 26, 1929, 418-444; 27, 1930, 485-494.

149. McDowell, E. D., *Educational and Emotional Adjustments of Stuttering Children.* New York: Teachers College Bureau of Publications, 1928.

150. McDougall, W., *Of the Words and Personality.* Character and Personality, 1932, 1, 3-16.

151. McGinnis, M. A., *Speech Training and Mental Hygiene Method for the Correction of Stammering.* Yearbook American Speech Correction Assn., Madison, Wis.: College Typing Co., 1930.

152. Meltzer, H., *Personality Differences between Stuttering and Non-Stuttering Children As Indicated by the Rorschach Test.* Psychology Bulletin, 30, 1933, 726-727.

153. Milisen, R. L., and Johnson, W., *Comparative Study of Stutterers, Former Stutterers, and Normal Speakers Whose Handedness Has Been Changed.* Arch. Speech, 1, 1936, 61-86.

154. Milisen, R. L., and Johnson, W., *A Further Comparative Study of Stutterers, Former Stutterers, and Normal Speakers Whose Handedness Has Been Changed.* Year-

book American Speech Correction Assn., Madison, Wis.: College Typing Co., 1936.

155. Morgan, J. J. B., *Psychology of Abnormal People*. New York: Longmans, Green and Co., 1928.

156. Murphy, G., and Jensen, F., *Approaches to Personality*. New York: Coward-McCann, Inc., 1932.

157. Murray, E., *Disintegration of Breathing and Eye Movements in Stutterers During Silent Reading and Reasoning*. Psych. Monographs, 43, 1931, 218-275.

158. Olson, W. L., *The Waiver of Signature in Personal Reports*. Journal Applied Psychology, 1936, 20, 442-51.

159. Orton, S. T., *Reading, Writing and Speech Problems in Children*. New York: W. W. Norton Co., 1937.

160. Orton, S. T., *Training the Left-Handed*. Hygeia, 5, 1927, 451-4.

161. Orton, S. T., *Studies in Stuttering, Introduction*. Arch. Neurology and Psychiatry, 18, 1927, 671-672.

162. Orton, S. T., *Word Blindness in School Children*. Arch. Neurology and Psychiatry, 14, 1925, 581-615.

163. Palmer, M. F., and Gillett, A. M., *Sex Differences in the Cardiac Rhythms of Stutterers*. Journal Speech Disorders, 3, 1938, 3-12.

164. Parker, H. T., *Defects of Speech in School Children*. Melbourne, Australia: Melbourne University Press, 1932.

165. Parsons, B. S., *Lefthandedness*. New York: The Macmillan Co., 1924.

166. Pearson, K., *On The Correlation of Characters Not Quantitatively Measurable*. Philosophical Transaction of the Royal Society of London. Series A, 195, 1900, 1-47.

167. Peters, C. A., *A Study of Mirror Reading in Speech Defectives and Normal Speakers*. Arch. of Speech, 1, 1936, 48-60.

168. Pinard, J. W., *Tests of Perseveration*. British Journal Psychology, 23, 1932, 114-126.

169. Pollock, C. A., *A Workable Program for Meeting Our Responsibilities in Speech Correction and Improvement in the Public Schools*. Yearbook American Speech Correction Assn., Madison, Wis.: College Typing Co., 1931.

170. Pressey, S. L., *A Group Scale for Investigating the Emo-*

tions. Journal Abnormal and Social Psychology, 16, 1921, 55-64.

171. Prince, M., *The Unconscious*. New York: The Macmillan Co., 2nd ed., 1924.

172. Quinan, C., *Sinistrality in Relation to High Blood Pressure and Defects of Speech*. Arch. International Medicine, 27, 1921, 255-261.

173. Raubicheck, L., *Correction of Stammering in Big School Systems*. Yearbook American Speech Correction Assn., Madison, Wis.: College Typing Co., 1930.

174. Raubicheck, L., *Handicapped and Underprivileged Children: Speech Improvement*. In Report to New York City Sup't of Schools. New York: Board of Education, 1934.

175. Robbins, S., *Breath Control in Stammering*. Yearbook American Speech Correction Assn., Madison, Wis.: College Typing Co., 1930.

176. Robbins, S., and Stinchfield, S. M., *A Dictionary of Terms Dealing with Disorders of Speech*. Boston: Expression Co., 1931.

177. Robbins, S. A., *Plethysmographic Study of Shock and Stammering*. American Journal Psychology, 48, 1919, 3-19.

178. Robbins, S., *Relation between the Short Auditory Memory Span Disability and Disorders of Speech*. Yearbook American Speech Correction Assn., Madison, Wis.: College Typing Co., 1932.

179. Robbins, S., *Stammering and Its Treatment*. Boston: Boston Stammerers' Institute.

180. Robinson, F. F., *The Role of Eye Movements in Reading with an Evaluation of Techniques for Their Improvement*. University of Iowa Studies, Series in Aims and Progress of Research, No. 39, 1933.

181. Rogers, J. F., *The Speech Defective School Child*. Office of Education, Washington, D. C., Bulletin No. 7, 1931.

182. Root, H. R., *Survey of Speech Defectives in the Public Elementary Schools of South Dakota*. Elementary School Journal, 26, 1926, 531-541.

183. Rouma, G., *La Parole et les Troubles de la Parole*. Paris: 1907.

184. Sachs, M. W., *Zur Aetiologie das Stotterns*. Klin. Woch., 37, 1924, 113.

185. Schroeder, P. L., and Ackerson, L., *Relationship of Personality and Behavior Difficulties to Disorders of Speech*. Yearbook American Speech Correction Assn., Madison, Wis.: College Typing Co., 1930.

186. Scripture, E. W., *Behavioristic Aspects of Speech Defects*. Journal Speech Education, 10, 1914.

187. Scripture, E. W., *Stuttering and Lisping*. (2nd ed.). New York: The Macmillan Co., 1923.

188. Seth, G., *An Experimental Study of the Control of the Mechanism of Speech and in Particular of That Respiration in Stuttering Subjects*. British Journal Psychology, 24, 1934, 375-388.

189. *Shorter Oxford Dictionary*. Oxford: Clarendon Press, 1933.

190. Solomon, M., *Incipient Stuttering in a Pre-school Child Aged Two and One-Half Years*. Yearbook American Speech Correction Assn., Madison, Wis.: College Typing Co., 1932.

191. Solomon, M., *The Psychology of Stuttering*. Journal Speech Disorders, 3, 1938, 59-61.

192. Spencer, D., *Fulcra of Conflict*. Yonkers-on-Hudson: World Book Co., 939.

193. Ssikorski, J. A., *Ueber das Stottern*. Berlin: Hirschwald, 1891.

194. Stagner, Ross, *Validity and Reliability of the Bernreuter Personality Inventory*. Journal Abnormal and Social Psychology, 28, 1934.

195. St. Claire, W. F., and Seegers, J. C., *Certain Aspects of the Validity of the Bernreuter Personality Inventory*. Journal Educational Psychology, 28, 1937, 530-40.

196. Starr, H. E., *The Hydrogen Ion Concentration of the Mixed Saliva Considered As an Index of Fatigue and of Emotional Excitation, and Applied to a Study of the Metabolic Etiology of Stuttering*. American Journal Psychology, 33, 1923, 394-418.

197. Starr, H. E., *Psychological Concomitants of Higher Alveolar Carbon Dioxide*, etc., Psychol. Clinic, 17, 1928, 1.

198. Steel, M. S., *How Dr. G. Hudson Makuen Treated Stammering.* Yearbook American Speech Correction Assn., Madison, Wis.: College Typing Co., 1930.

199. Steer, M. D., *The General Intelligence of College Stutterers.* School and Society, 44, 1936, 862-864.

200. Steer, M. D., and Johnson, W., *An Objective Study of the Relationship between Psychological Factors and the Severity of Stuttering.* Journal American and Social Psychology, 31, 1936, 36-46.

201. Steer, M. D., *Symptomatologies of Young Stutterers.* Journal Speech Disorders, 2, 1937, 3-37.

202. Stekel, W., *Nervoese Augszustaende und ihre Behandlung.* Vienna, 1908.

203. Stern, W., *General Psychology from the Personalistic Standpoint.* New York: The Macmillan Co., 1938.

204. Stinchfield, S. M., *Psychology of Speech.* Boston: Expression Co.

205. Stinchfield, S. M., *Speech Disorders.* New York: Harcourt, Brace & Co., 1934.

206. Stinchfield, S. M., *Speech Pathology.* Boston: Expression Co., 1928.

207. Stivers, C. G., *Oral Stammering.* Yearbook American Speech Correction Assn., Madison, Wis.: College Typing Co., 1930.

208. Stoddard, C. B., *The Correction of Stammering in Detroit.* Yearbook American Speech Correction Assn., Madison, Wis.: College Typing Co., 1930.

209. Stoddard, C. B., *A Study of Stammerers.* Detroit Board of Education Pub. 1925.

210. Stratton, L. D., *A Factor in the Etiology of a Sub-Breathing Stammerer.* Journal Comparative Psychology, 4, 1924, 325-345.

211. Strong, E. K., *Procedure for Scoring and Interest Test.* Psychology Clinic, 19, 1930, 63-72.

212. Swift, W. B., *The Mental Imagery of Stutterers.* Journal Abnormal Psychology, April, May, 1917.

213. Symonds, P. M., *Diagnosing Personality and Conduct.* New York: Century Co., 1931.

214. Symonds, P. M., *Needed Research in Diagnosing Per-*

sonality and Conduct. Journal Educational Research, 24, 1931, 175-187.

215. Symonds, P. M., and Jackson, C. E., *An Adjustment Survey.* Journal Educational Research, 21, 1930, 321-330.

216. Ten Cate, M. J., *Ueber die Untersuchung der Athmung bei Sprachfehlern.* Monatach f. Sprachheikunde, 12, 1902, 247-259.

217. Terman, L. M., *The Measurement of Personality.* Science, 1934, 89, 605-608.

218. *Tests of Personality and Character.* Review of Educational Research, 2, No. 3, 1932.

219. Thorndike, E. L., *Mental and Social Measurement.* New York: Teachers College Bureau of Publications, 1913.

220. Thorndike, E. L., *Unity or Purity in Traits and Tests.* Occupations, 12, 1934, 57-60.

221. Thorpe, L. P., *Psychological Mechanisms of Stuttering.* Journal General Psychology, 19, 1938, 97-109.

222. Thurstone, L. L., and Thurstone, T. G., *A Neurotic Inventory.* Journal Social Psychology, 1, 1930, 3-39.

223. Timme, W., *Lectures on Endocrinology.* New York: P. B. Hoeber, Inc., 1932.

224. Tompkins, E., *Stuttering.* Ped. Sem., 23, 1923, 155.

225. Travis, L. E., *A Comparative Study of the Performance of Stutterers and Normal Speakers in Star Tracing.* Psych. Monographs, 39, 1928, 45-50.

226. Travis, L. E., *Diagnosis and Treatment of Stuttering Cases.* Yearbook American Speech Correction Assn., Madison, Wis.: College Typing Co., 1930.

227. Travis, L. E., *Disintegration of the Breathing Movements During Stuttering.* Arch. Neurology and Psychiatry, 18, 1927, 673-690.

228. Travis, L. E., *Speech Pathology.* In Handbook of Child Psychology (2nd ed.), C. Murchison, ed. Worcester, Mass.: Clark Univ. Press, 1933.

229. Travis, L. E., *Speech Pathology.* New York: D. Appleton-Century, 1931.

230. Travis, L. E., *Studies in Stuttering. II. Photographic Studies of the Voice in Stuttering.* Arch. Neurology and Psychiatry, 18, 1927, 998-1014.

231. Travis, L. E., and Dorsey, J. M., *Patellar Tendon Reflex Time in Psychiatric and Neurological Cases*. Arch. Neurology and Psychiatry, 22, 1929, 99-104.

232. Travis, L. E., Malamud, W., and Thayer, L. R., *Relationship between Physical Habitus and Stuttering*. Journal Abnormal Psychology, 29, 1934, 132-140.

233. Travis, V. A., *Study of the Horizontal Disintegration of Breathing During Stuttering*. Arch. Speech, 1, 1936, 157-169.

234. Traxler, A. E., *Use of Tests and Rating Devices in the Appraisal of Personality*. New York: Educational Records Bulletin, 23, 1938.

235. Trumper, M., *A Hemato-Respiratory Study of 101 Consecutive Cases of Stammering*. Philadelphia: University of Pennsylvania Press, 1928.

236. Twitmyer, E. B., *Stammering in Relation to Hemato-Respiratory Factors*. Quarterly Journal Speech, 1930, 278-283.

237. Van Riper, C., *The Quantitative Measurement of Laterality*. Journal Experimental Psychology, 28, 1935, 372-382.

238. Wallin, J. E. W., *A Census of Speech Defects*. School and Society, 3, 1916, 213.

239. Wallin, J. E. W., *Speech Defectives among Public School Pupils*. School and Society, 3, 1916, 213-216.

240. Wallin, J. E. W., *Theories of Stuttering*. Journal Applied Psychology, Dec. 1917, 349-367.

241. Warren, H. C., and Carmichael, L., *Elements of Human Psychology*. Boston: Houghton Mifflin Co., 1930.

242. Watson, G. B., *Mental Hygiene and Adjustment*. Chapter IV of Review of Educational Research, Washington, D. C.: Nat'l Education Assn., 1935.

243. Watson, G. B., *Next Steps in Personality Measurements*. Character and Personality, 1932, 2, 66-73.

244. Watson, J. B., *Behaviorism*. New York: W. W. Norton Co., 1925.

245. Wells, H. H., III, *The Measurement of Certain Aspects of Personality among Hard-of-Hearing Adults*. New York: Teachers College Bureau of Publications, 1930.

246. Wepman, J. M., *Is Stuttering Inherited?* Yearbook American Speech Correction Assn., Madison, Wis.: College Typing Co., 1934.

247. West, R., *A Neurological Test for Stutterers.* Journal Neurology and Psychology, 38, 1929, 114-123.

248. West, R., *Phenomenology of Stuttering.* Yearbook American Speech Correction Assn., Madison, Wis.: College Typing Co., 1930.

249. West, R., *Purposive Speaking.* New York: The Macmillan Co., 1924.

250. West, R., Kennedy, L., Carr., A., *Rehabilitation of Speech.* New York: Harper & Bros., 1937.

251. West, R., Nelson, S., and Berry, M., *The Heredity of Stuttering.* Quarterly Journal Speech, 25, 1939, 23-30.

252. Westphal, G., *An Experimental Study of Certain Motor Abilities of Stuttering.* University of Iowa Studies in Child Development, 4, 1933, 214, 221.

253. Wheeler, R. H., and Perkins, F. T., *Principles of Mental Development.* New York: Thos. Y. Crowell Co., 1932.

254. White House Conference Report. *The Handicapped Child.* New York: D. Appleton Century Co., 1930.

255. Wilson, J., *Why Stutterers React Favorably to Many Kinds of Treatment.* Yearbook American Speech Correction Assn., Madison, Wis.: College Typing Co., 1931.

256. Woodworth, R., *Contemporary Schools of Psychology.* New York: Ronald Press, 1931.

257. Woodworth, R., *Dynamic Psychology.* New York: Columbia University Press, 1918.

258. Woodworth, R., *Psychology.* New York: Henry Holt & Co., 1929.

259. *Woodworth-House Mental Hygiene Inventory.* New York: Psychological Corp.

INDEX OF NAMES

INDEX OF SUBJECTS